HUSBANDMEN
OF PLYMOUTH

HUSBANDMEN OF PLYMOUTH

Farms and Villages in the Old Colony, 1620-1692

DARRETT B. RUTMAN

Published for Plimoth Plantation by

BEACON PRESS • BOSTON

Illustrations by Eric G. Engstrom

*The publication of this book has been made possible through a grant
by the Society of Mayflower Descendants in the Commonwealth of
Massachusetts.*

Preface

WHEN FIRST INVITED by Plimoth Plantation to undertake this study, I was delighted. I had just completed my *Winthrop's Boston: Portrait of a Puritan Town*, and many ideas had suggested themselves over the five years of research on that work which found no place in the book. One of the ideas was that the "New England town" made so much of by historians was not, in reality, quite as it has so often been described; that the town was, at least in the seventeenth century, a straggling sort of place very different in appearance from that depicted by Thomas Jefferson Wertenbaker and others. I thought, too, that I should like to explore the differences between dynamic, bustling Boston and the seemingly more placid "country towns." Problems relating directly to agriculture had arisen. I had found no good account of agriculture which pinpointed the individual farmer and his day-by-day, week-by-week tasks, yet kept the individual within the context of the entire Atlantic commercial community—nothing between the antiquarian approach with its concern for unrelated minutiae and that of the professional historian concerned with broad trends. There were small but nagging problems associated with agricultural yields, land usage, the quick adoption of Indian corn by Englishmen generally prone to suspect strange foods, and the tendency of the settlers in America toward extensive agriculture at the very time that English writers were stressing intensive agriculture.

All of these, I felt, could be dealt with on the relatively small stage of the "Old Colony." And if I could not solve them to the utter and complete satisfaction of historians within the limits of the series—limitations on both length and style, for the series is designed quite rightly for the average reader as well as the professional historian—I could at least suggest solutions. This I have attempted to do.

I would be most remiss if I did not immediately acknowledge the assistance of Plimoth Plantation. The first suggestion for the volume came from Arthur G. Pyle, Education Director. David B. Freeman, Director, has given freely of his time in reading and criticizing the manuscript and seeing it into print. And the Plantation has placed at my disposal its microfilm of certain manuscript materials and of the research reports done for it over the past years. Those prepared by Jane Strickland Hussey, covering such diverse subjects as "Pilgrim Herb Gardens," "Indian Gardens," and "Children's Activities," have been particularly valuable. The Plantation has allowed me access to correspondence connected with the Plymouth village restoration which touched upon agriculture; at second hand, for example, officials of the Plymouth County Extension Service and the American Poultry Historical Society have aided me in identifying the dunghill cock which undoubtedly walked the streets of the Old Colony's villages. The staff of Walter Library at the University of Minnesota has been most helpful, while the University itself has placed research funds at my disposal, greatly facilitating the study. Mr. C. A. Jewell, Keeper, the Museum of English Rural Life at the University of Reading, England, has been of great help in supplying material for the illustrations. My friend and colleague, Professor Rodney C. Loehr, a past president of the Agricultural History Society, was kind enough to read and criticize the manuscript.

Lastly, and in lieu of a dedication, I wish to acknowledge

Preface

my great debt to Laurence and Jane Rutman. Among the very many things which they did for their son was taking him as a city boy to live on a Pennsylvania farm, introducing him to mysteries denied to so many in today's urban America.

D. B. R.

University of Minnesota

Contents

Illustrations

HUSBANDMEN
OF PLYMOUTH

CHAPTER ONE

"By Which Means
They Were Scattered
All over the Bay"

ON JULY 5, 1664, JAMES WYATT of Taunton in the colony of New Plymouth drove his wooden, two-wheeled cart out of his barnyard toward a meadow some miles away. There was a glint of dew on the grass, but the sun would burn that away long before he reached his field and began methodically swinging the long-handled scythe which lay on the cart. Except for his own sweat, there would be no trace of moisture when, at evening, he put aside the scythe to load the cart with grass he had cut two days before.

James Wyatt as a person is almost unknown in history. His name appears now and again in the records of his town and colony—as constable of Taunton, surveyor-of-highways, grandjuryman, lieutenant of militia, selectman, and deputy to the general court. He was not an important figure of the times, however. We know precisely where he was on this July 5 only because he was seized by a stroke and died in the meadow, facts which a hastily gathered coroner's jury dutifully recorded.[1] But the scene of James Wyatt driving out to his meadow, a prosaic, commonplace scene escaping all notice but for the fact of his death, was typical. One can imagine hundreds of other men doing exactly the same thing at exactly the same time. For James Wyatt was a farmer in the haymaking season, and the colony of New Plymouth was a colony of farmers.

It was not purposefully so. Forty-four years earlier the

3

first Englishmen had landed at Plymouth to establish the colony. They had not come as farmers, a fact which has been frequently pointed out.[2] Some were religious dissenters from English ways who had left their English homes for the Netherlands and spent long years working as printers or clothworkers in the town of Leyden prior to embarking for America. Others came directly from England, but for the most part from London, where they had been artisans and tradesmen. Their ship, the *Mayflower*, carried no cattle or sheep, no oxen or horses. Indeed, the leaders anticipated that furs and fish would form the economic basis of the colony. How, then, did Plymouth become an agricultural colony? From whom did the settlers learn their farming? How great was their commitment to the soil? These are the first questions to be answered.

The men of the *Mayflower* were not farmers, true. Yet the soil was never very far in the background of a seventeenth-century Englishman. The Leyden pilgrims had originally come from agricultural counties in England, leaving farms and villages behind when they departed for the Netherlands; London, having doubled in size during the reign of Queen Elizabeth, was an adopted home for many residents whose origins lay in rural England. Scratch either a Leyden clothworker or a London tradesman, therefore, and you would likely find the son of a country "husbandman." William Bradford, for example, spent his years in Leyden as a weaver but grew up in the farm atmosphere of southern Yorkshire and, at the time he left for the Netherlands, described himself and others as "used to a plain country life and the innocent trade of husbandry." William Brewster, a printer in Leyden, was the son of the steward and bailiff of Scrooby Manor, Nottinghamshire, grew up in a country-manor atmosphere, and was himself steward of the manor. Edward Winslow, a London printer, came from a Worcestershire yeoman family. John Howland, a Londoner, seems to have had an Essex farm background.[3]

The artisans and tradesmen of the *Mayflower* were not, therefore, completely ignorant of farm life; hence, they carried an agricultural tradition across the ocean with them. Neither were they completely unprepared for agricultural activity on landing in the New World. They realized the necessity of growing food in order to subsist, even while looking to fish and furs for their profit. Consequently, they loaded aboard the *Mayflower* hoes and mattocks with which to break the ground, and seeds to plant. The rapidity with which chickens, goats, and pigs appeared in large numbers at New Plymouth makes it quite probable that at least some such barnyard animals were crowded on the ship as well. In selecting a site for their town the settlers took into account agricultural capabilities, choosing Plymouth because the abandoned Indian cornfields on the site indicated fertility and promised easy cultivation without the laborious task of clearing trees.[4] And although they arrived too late in the season to plant in 1620, the settlers turned immediately to the soil during the following spring, a Pilgrim commentator noting that on March 19 and 20 "we digged our grounds, and sowed our garden seed."[5] That first year some twenty-six acres of corn, barley, and peas were planted. The following year almost sixty acres were under cultivation, *"besides their gardens well replenished with useful fruits."* In 1623, 184 acres were laid out and presumably planted.[6]

If the first comers anticipated finding their sustenance (but not their profit) in the soil, their early endeavors were nevertheless outside the English tradition. In England the yeoman worked his own ground for his own profit; the hired farm laborer, although working for another, worked for his own bread. But in Plymouth the settlers at first worked the soil in common and shared its products. They did so not by choice, however, but of necessity, the financial arrangements with the London merchants who underwrote the initial expenses of their settlement dictating the agricultural organization. The settlers as a body were committed to work for the profit of a joint stock company consisting of themselves, investing their persons and their labor in the enterprise, and those London merchants who invested their money.[7] Artificial "families" were created during the first winter in New England as unattached men were joined to natural families. Each such grouping was housed together and cultivated its own garden plot laid out in conjunction with the house, the size of the garden depending upon the number within the "family." But all hands were required to work in the larger fields laid out beyond the village, the produce of which went into a common storehouse.[8] Livestock was also common property at first. "Greate cattle" arrived in 1624, when Edward Winslow, who had journeyed briefly to England, returned with three heifers and a bull for the use of the whole community. More cattle came on succeeding ships—a red heifer sent over by merchant James Sherley for "the benefitt of the poore of the Towne," two steers, another bull, and four black heifers—while the natural increase added three heifers and two calves by the spring of 1627.[9]

Few were happy with the "common course and condition," as Governor Bradford called the communal agricultural structure. Its strangeness, the fact that it was so contrary to the agricultural tradition they knew, was discomfiting. There were drones who idled while others labored, and in a land where every hand was needed to survive there were women who "would allege weakness and inability" to avoid weeding and hoeing. There was a very human tendency to work less for the common good than one would work for one's own good. And there was, finally, a dislike for the

London merchants, with whom relations were far from ami-
cable, Governor Bradford writing in 1625 that many of the
colonists "protest they will never build houses, fence grounds,
or plant fruits for those, who not only forsake them, but
use them as enemies." [10]

The crop which the settlers came to rely upon during the
earliest years was strange and discomfiting, too. The barley
and field peas planted in 1621 were traditional English
crops planted in roughly the traditional English manner,
the settlers breaking up the soil as best they could with their
hoes, scattering seeds broadcast, then hoeing again to cover
the seeds.[11] Similarly, the gardens were planted with traditional English vegetables—garden peas, cabbages, radishes,
carrots, garlic, onions, leeks, melons, artichokes, a variety of
herbs, skirret (a root similar to but sweeter than the parsnip).
But the corn planted that year was Indian corn, indigenous
to the New World.

Contrary to the stereotype, the Indian of the Northeast
was less a hunter and fisherman and more an agricultural
being. He cleared the land about his village by burning the
grass and underbrush, killing the larger trees by burning
their bases or girdling (cutting circularly around the trees,
through bark and cambium layer, close to the ground).
Readying the cleared "fields" for planting was a community
affair. The men and women of the village gathered at the
end of March or early April to break up the soil, not of an
entire field but of small circles two feet across and two to
three feet apart, each circle hilled toward the center. Once
broken up—or, if a previously cultivated field, once the
litter of the past year had been removed and the soil of
the old hills stirred up and softened—the field became
women's work. Very carefully they set grains of seed corn
into the center of each circle, "deep enough that it may have
a strong root . . . yet not too deep, lest they bury it, and

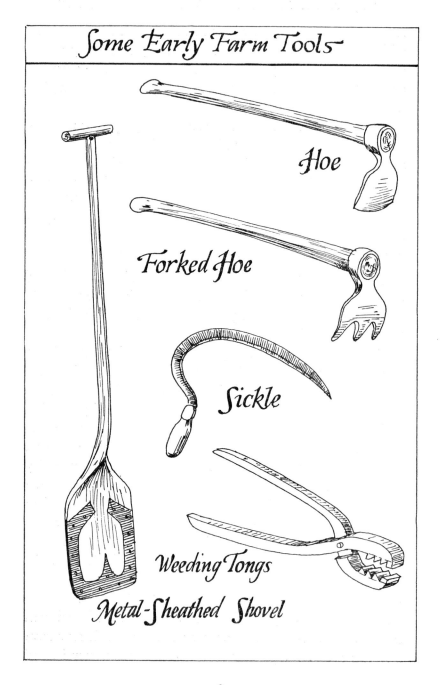

Hoe

Forked Hoe

Sickle

Weeding Tongs

Metal-Sheathed Shovel

it never come up." [12] Two plantings several weeks apart were usual in order to prolong the period of fresh corn in the fall. Here and there along the coast the women fertilized the corn by setting a small herringlike fish, the alewife, with the seed, a trick passed on to the men of Plymouth. As the first corn shoots broke the surface a few weeks after planting, the women descended on the fields again, carefully planting three or four bean seeds around the young corn. Corn and beans grew together, the beans climbing on the cornstalks. Sometimes squash and pumpkin seeds were planted in the hills, their vines trailing across the uncultivated land between.

All summer long the Indian woman worked at her task, using a crude clamshell hoe to scratch out weeds and cultivate the earth, pushing the soil always toward the center and making the hills higher and higher. In midsummer the smallest and least fruitful cornstalks were plucked up, their sap sucked out by the Indians as children in sugar country suck the sap of the cane. In August the beans began coming in. Toward fall the squashes and pumpkins were taken up, for a while becoming the mainstay of the Indian diet. The corn was the last to be harvested, the Indians leaving the ears on the stalks well into fall that the kernels might grow as large as possible, accepting the starchiness of overripe corn in the interest of greater quantity. Even so, there was little enough; the varicolored ears (black, red, blue, green, and occasionally the familiar yellow) were short and nubbly, no longer than four or five inches. Forty to forty-five bushels were raised by the Indian woman working approximately two and a half acres containing some nine hundred hills. Picked and shocked, the kernels worked from the cobs by the children of the family, then boiled and beaten to make bread or porridge, the gathered corn fed the family through the winter and into the spring, when the cycle began again. [13]

9

The Plymouth settlers of 1620, while exploring Cape Cod prior to landing at Plymouth, had seen the Indian corn-fields and the harvested grain stored in baskets. Several of the *Mayflower's* seamen and at least one of the settlers (Stephen Hopkins) had been in the New World before and presumably they told the others of the value of corn, for the exploring party carried off ten bushels of corn and a bag of beans for seed.[14] From the Indian Squanto they learned how to plant Indian-style during the spring of 1621, a story familiar to every schoolchild.[15] But as with their communal organization, the settlers adopted corn out of need rather than desire. Corn was new and strange, alien and, therefore, to the English mind, inferior to the more traditional grains. English writers of the time were warning of the doleful effects of eating corn, while as late as 1660, John Winthrop, Jr., of nearby Connecticut would assume a defensive attitude when writing of corn for English readers.[16] Corn was, moreover, an arduous crop. To tend it as the Indian women did, required assiduous hoeing to keep down the weeds, a labor unnecessary with English grains. Edward Winslow wrote of the difficulties attendant on corn in his 1624 tract *Good Newes from New-England*: Corn, or maize, he noted, "will not be procured without good labour and diligence; especially at seed time, when it must also be watched by night, to keep the wolves from the fish." [17] A ballad attributed to the 1620's catalogued additional dangers which had to be watched for and combated:

> Our corn being planted and seed being sown,
> The worms destroy much before it is grown;
> And when it is growing, some spoil there is made
> By birds and by squirrels that pluck up the blade;
> E'en when it is grown to full corn in the ear
> It is often destroyed by raccoons and deer.[18]

All this had to be borne, however, for English crops did poorly when first planted. Barley, for example, required a finer breaking up of the soil than the settlers could manage without proper plows and draft animals; hence in 1621 it was but "indifferent good." The field peas that year were "not worth the gathering," having been planted too late, probably as a result of the length of time needed to break up the soil with hoes. "I think," Winslow wrote, "if we had cattle to till the ground, it would be more profitable, and better agreeable to the soil, to sow wheat, rye, barley, pease, and oats, then to set mays." But one made the best of what one had, and Winslow assured his English readers that "Indian corn, even the coarsest, maketh as pleasant meat as Rice." [19]

Corn soon lost its strangeness for the settlers. It was a rich source of food for men and animals and so remained a major part of the early American scene. But we would be sadly mistaken if we were to assume that corn monopolized that scene. In Plymouth, corn, so vital for survival in the first years, decreased in importance after 1624 and 1625, when English grains were successfully harvested. Grain, not corn, became the basic cash crop; corn was reduced to food for animals and men of the "baser sort," as Madam Sarah Kemble Knight's disdainful use of the phrase "Indian fare" early in the eighteenth century indicates.[20] One can conjecture that the remarkable speed with which "Indian" was accepted even to this extent by Englishmen generally reluctant to indulge in such innovations of diet was a result of the fact that grain came to represent substantial profit. Only the well-to-do could afford to spurn the rougher fare and consume profit; lesser men would adjust their palates to their pocketbooks.

Similarly, we would be mistaken if we were to assume

that the colonists continued to plant Indian-style. Nowhere in the New World did Englishmen adopt Indian ways completely. On the contrary, they everywhere adapted the New World and its ways to their own English ways. Hence in Plymouth, as we shall see, the Indian methods of corn cultivation adopted in the first years were subsequently modified by English (and less arduous) ways.

If Indian corn remained, that other discomfiting factor of the early years, the "common course and condition," was quickly dispensed with. After a particularly hard winter in 1622–1623 each family was assigned corn land of its own on the basis of one acre per family member, the family to keep whatever it raised, less a proportion to be used "for the maintenance of Public Officers, Fishermen, etc." The next year (1624), the assignments were permanently allotted and became private property.[21] In 1627 "great lots" were allocated on the basis of twenty acres per person, a single man receiving twenty acres, the head of a family twenty acres for himself, his wife, and each of his children and servants—a generous allotment considering the agricultural tools and techniques of the time. The same year the cattle, swine, and goats were divided among the inhabitants. In theory twelve artificial families each received an allotment, the individual members of the families having a share in the care and profit of the animals. In practice, however, the natural families— the Allertons, Brewsters, Standishes, Winslows—took possession of the stock, buying out the single men who were attached to the family for the purposes of the division. For the time being the meadows around Plymouth village remained common property, but even these fell to private ownership by the early 1630's.[22]

The end of communal agriculture was a boon to the settlement. "It made all hands very industrious," Governor Bradford recorded; more corn was planted than heretofore, and "the women now went willingly into the field, and took their little ones with them." Food shortages which had plagued the settlers during the first years became a thing of the past. The settlers now had corn to spare and used it as money, trading "one with another for small things." The colony as a whole began sending surplus corn north to the Maine coast, buying furs to send to England. If secure, however, the settlement was still small and basically unprosperous, its people burdened by debts owed the original English backers and without the means to purchase from England the clothing, household goods, weapons, and tools which they could not make for themselves. In 1627 there were fewer than 200 persons in the colony, all living within the single village of New Plymouth. Of the great lots allocated that year, only those nearest the village were placed under cultivation; the law allowed those with lots at a distance to plant on the unused nearer lots belonging to others. To the leadership fish and fur were still looked upon as the most probable sources of profit; the land itself was looked to for little more than subsistence—this despite the hint of profit from the export of corn and the fact that fish and fur had thus far failed to live up to expectation. In 1630 the situation had not changed. There were perhaps 250 people living "well without want" but well without luxury.[23] Their cultivated acres were still grouped around tiny Plymouth village. For the rest, it was, as an early comer had written, a "pity . . . to see so many [naturally] goodly fields, and so well seated, without men to dress and manure the same."[24]

Prosperity came to Plymouth with the founding of Massachusetts Bay and was linked not to the colony's fur trading and fishing but to its farming. In 1630 John Winthrop led 700 settlers into the area immediately north of Plymouth. The towns of Boston, Charlestown, Lynn, Watertown, Roxbury, and Dorchester were founded. In 1631 and 1632, 800

13

more settlers arrived in the Bay colony. Newcomers made their appearance during the remainder of the decade at a rate of 1,000 to 3,000 a year. What has been termed the "great migration" was under way as Englishmen, for a variety of economic, religious, and political reasons, poured out of their tight little island. The newcomers in Massachusetts needed foodstuffs to carry them through the first year or two, sawed timbers to build their houses with, cattle to start their herds, draft animals to open fields, and for the most part the already-established settlers in the Bay area and elsewhere supplied these needs.[25] The men of Plymouth were quick to take advantage of the market created by the new settlements. Overland and on small coasters they carried their agricultural goods north to Boston to be exchanged for tools, clothing, cooking utensils, candles—all the products of England which Plymouth had, for the most part, done without during the first decade.

The prosperity was immediately in evidence. Land values jumped. In 1630 a house and garden in Plymouth were sold for nine pounds sterling; five years later the equivalent house and garden were sold for twenty-three pounds. Produce values showed even greater percentage increases, with livestock values far in the lead—a single cow selling for twenty-four pounds in 1636, three times the price in England; a pair of oxen for sixty pounds; a horse for forty pounds.[26]

That profits could be made on the land drew the settlers out of Plymouth village, scattering them, in Bradford's words, "all over the Bay." [27] The more distant great lots, ignored since the division of 1627, were put to use, at first for cattle as families living in Plymouth village sent their growing herds north or south to graze on natural meadows and marshlands under the care of a boy or servant. Soon families began quitting the village entirely, moving permanently to the great lots. Some of the leaders resisted the trend. To Governor Bradford it was "the ruin of New England" that "those that had lived so long together in Christian and comfortable fellowship must now part and suffer many divisions." But when even leaders, men like John Alden, Myles Standish, Thomas Prence, and Jonathan Brewster, took their families beyond Jones River to live in what is now Duxbury, "there was no longer any holding them together." [28] The Duxbury settlers organized a church separate from Plymouth's in 1632, and in 1637 Duxbury was recognized as a separate town. So great was the dispersal that some feared (without real foundation) that Plymouth village was "like to be dispeopled" entirely, a possibility to be prevented at all cost. In 1636, in order to bolster Plymouth, the leaders allotted "some good farms" north of Duxbury "to special persons that would promise to live" in the village. "But alas," Bradford wrote, "this remedy proved worse than the disease; for within a few years those that had thus got footing there rent themselves away" and became the separate town of Marshfield.[29] Families moving south from Massachusetts Bay or coming directly from England expanded the colony still more, settling Scituate, to the north of Marshfield, Sandwich, Barnstable, and Yarmouth on Cape Cod, and, far to the west, Taunton and Rehoboth—all before 1643. By that year there were approximately 1,800 people in the colony.[30]

The prosperity of the 1630's, with the consequent enlargement of the colony in terms both of people and of land occupied, was feverish. Its basis was faulty, however. Plymouth's market for cattle and grain depended upon the influx of newcomers into Massachusetts Bay, and to a lesser extent Plymouth colony itself, and the purchase and consumption of the agricultural surplus by these newcomers. So long as the newcomers continued to arrive, the prosperity lasted. In

1639 and 1640, however, the number of newcomers slackened, and in 1641 the great migration to all intents and purposes ended, largely as a result of a more favorable political and religious outlook in England. Massachusetts' economy—having developed on the same basis as Plymouth's—broke in the spring and summer of 1641 as cattle prices dropped abruptly from twenty and thirty pounds a head to four and five, wheat from seven shillings a bushel to four, Indian corn from five shillings to three, ultimately to nothing. Plymouth's economy followed, although being one step removed from the immediate catastrophe the decline was delayed. Grain prices broke in 1642, but cattle prices, dropping that year, partially recovered and held inexplicably firm until the late summer of 1644, when prices plummeted, a cow selling for thirteen pounds sterling in August and three pounds in November. That cattle prices held up for so long shortened the period of acute depression in Plymouth, for by 1644 and 1645 Massachusetts Bay merchants had discovered a market for grain overseas, sending wheat to the Azores, Madeira, and the coast of Spain. Grain prices rose as the new market developed, and Plymouth grain was again dispatched to Boston, now to be exported. When the Massachusetts men opened an even broader market for agricultural goods in the Caribbean, sending beef, grain, flour, even livestock on the hoof to Caribbean planters too busy planting sugar to plant foodstuffs, the stability of Plymouth's economy was assured.[31]

The post-depression economy was, on the surface, much what it had been in the 1630's, Plymouth men sending their surplus cattle and grain north to the Bay to exchange for goods imported from England. But where cattle had dominated the market before, grain was now the more important. Prices reflected the shift, for while wheat and corn prices rose to just below the levels of 1642, cattle prices, although improved, remained low. As a result the Plymouth farmer turned more to grain, hitching cattle which might once have gone north to the Bay to plows and transforming meadows into fields of wheat, rye, barley, and oats. Cattle were more regularly pastured than in the first two decades lest the herds infringe on cultivated fields. Winter feeding came to be practiced, as the sale of a farm to William Hanbury indicates: John Brown, the seller, was to be allowed to make use of the barn and outhouses of the farm during the ensuing winter "to winter his cattell and lay his fodder in." [32] The trend away from Indian agricultural methods was quickened, too. Less Indian corn and more English grain were planted. Fields, even to some extent cornfields, tended to be regularly laid out, fenced, carefully fertilized, plowed, harrowed, and sown, all in roughly the English manner. Where, for example, the first comers had fertilized with fish Indian-style, the farmers of the 1640's and on tended to revert to the traditional manure.[33]

It did not happen all at once in every part of the colony, of course. The tendency was a gradual one and there were clear differences between towns as a result of their differing ages. The development of any single town was basically the same as that of Plymouth village itself, however, and was closely connected to the handling of cattle. In the earliest years of settlement all cattle grazed together in a common herd about the village, roaming the meadows under the sometimes careless eyes of the boys of the settlement. But, as we have seen, the development of a market for cattle in Massachusetts Bay and the subsequent increase of the size of the herd resulted in change. Some families sent their cattle away to their great lots, the family itself remaining for a time in Plymouth. Not all of the cattle were dispatched, for draft animals and milk cows were needed closer to home. Hence, the common herd remained a part of the village scene under the care of a town herdsman from spring to fall, grazing during the day and being brought home for care and milking in the evening. That some cattle—the "dry cattle" normally meant for market—were sent abroad while some remained in the village created a distinction between animals on the basis of use. Ultimately many of those families which had sent dry cattle away tended themselves to leave the village, founding new towns. But the distinction between animals remained. Those Plymouth families which did not leave the village still had dry cattle in addition to milk and draft animals. The latter continued to be grazed on ungranted and therefore "common" land about the village in a town herd until the mid-1640's, when the town herd disappeared and the home cattle were pastured on the lands of individual owners. And the dry cattle, as before, were sent abroad to graze semiwild on distant vacant land, although at times brought into the village during the winter. The quantity of vacant land within the town steadily decreased, however, being granted to individuals who settled and improved the land and frequently withdrew from Plymouth altogether to form new towns. The result was that the dry cattle were sent farther and farther afield until eventually there was no place for them. With that the free grazing herd disappeared, market cattle being limited to the land of the owner as milk and draft cattle had been earlier, or they were sent to another town to be kept on shares, owner and keeper each receiving half of the "increase" or offspring of the animals.

The pattern discerned in Plymouth village was repeated in every town of the Old Colony—free grazing common herd, the separation of dry cattle from the town herd, the disappearance of the town herd, and, ultimately, of the semiwild herd of dry cattle. A steady enlargement of the cultivated proportion of the land of a town and the tendency

within every town to a more and more English-style farming (with its accent on ordered fields) paralleled this cattle
pattern, indeed, in part caused it, for free grazing and
orderly cultivation did not mix, and a tendency toward the
latter invariably worked against the former. At any given
time the various towns of the colony were in a different stage
of the evolving pattern. The newer towns were rougher and
cruder in appearance, their fields smaller and less regularly
laid out, their dependence on common activity (such as the
town herd) greater, and their preoccupation more with cattle
than with crops. The older towns were more English in appearance, less concerned with cattle and more given over to
field crops. Although risking oversimplification, we can sum-
marize the general tendency as a progression within each
town from cattle to cultivation.[34]

Without the exorbitant prices of the 1630's and the
plethora of English goods which those prices had purchased,
Plymouth's people turned from the 1640's on more to
articles of their own making. Sheep were introduced for
their wool, which spinsters turned into thread and weavers
wove into coarse cloth. Hides from slaughtered cattle were
tanned by local artisans and turned into leather for harnesses,
shoes, and work aprons. A local mine and furnace turned out
iron, which blacksmiths formed into crude tools and utensils.
The result was a lessened dependence upon Massachusetts
Bay, although by no means economic independence. The Bay
Colony was the only significant market for Plymouth's produce, a fact acknowledged by Plymouth's General Court
when, in 1643, it ordered that bushel and half-bushel measures "made by the Bay standard" be procured in order "that
our measures [may] be made according to them."[35] And
the Bay Colony was the source of a vast array of items which
local artisans and handicrafters could not produce.

Some settlers, particularly those in the inland towns,

19

sent their agricultural products directly to the Boston fairs, driving their cattle overland or carting their grain along the primitive roads which linked Rehoboth and Taunton to the Bay capital, bringing home buttons, hats, knives, and such purchased in Boston's shops.[36] More often than not, however, the individual settler in Plymouth was linked to Boston through small merchants like Stephen Hopkins and John Barnes of Plymouth village, Nicholas Nickerson of Yarmouth, John Floyd and Thomas Tarte of Scituate. The home of such a merchant, housing both the merchant's family and his wares, was a veritable general store. The inventory of John Barnes's estate (1671) indicates the diversity of goods offered for sale to friends and neighbors: nine hats and five "blacke silke hatt bands," five pairs of gloves and "a pair of mittens and a paire of blacke Garters," six shirts, a variety of brass and iron pans, kettles, and skillets, pewterware and "a Cokernutt sett with pewter," cloth and buttons and "a pound of thrid a knife and kniting needles," augers and sickles, handsaws and plow irons.[37]

The merchants' world was a world of credit. The individual villager in Plymouth, desiring this or that, obtained goods from the merchant's stock, promising to pay the purchase price of so many pounds, shillings, and pence at a future date. Subsequently he would satisfy the debt in "country pay"—a cow, or so many bushels of wheat or oats, whatever he had to offer and the merchant cared to accept. The merchant, for his part, obtained his stock from a Boston merchant on credit, eventually paying his debt by sending to the Bostonian the grain and cattle he had received from the neighbors who patronized his "store." The Boston merchant, in turn, obtained his goods from an English merchant on credit, more often than not promising to send agricultural products to the Caribbean or Madeira to be traded for sugar or wine, the sugar or wine to be sent on to the London merchant.[38] The Plymouth merchant's profits in the trade were large. Stephen Hopkins, for example, purchased a mirror in Boston for nine pence and sold it in Plymouth for sixteen pence; John Barnes, in 1640, bought rye at four shillings a bushel in Plymouth and sold it for five shillings.[39] (Prices were invariably recorded in specie, albeit they represented what were in effect barter transactions.) But given the vital nature of the merchant's role in connecting the fields of Plymouth with the vast Atlantic trading community and ultimately the English merchant supplying finished goods, such profits were not exorbitant. Without Hopkins, some Plymouth girl or young wife would have had to preen before a quiet pool of water rather than a mirror, and without Barnes some farmer's rye would have rotted in the field rather than pay for necessary English goods.

In the years after the break in the economy the population of the colony still grew, but growth was neither the sixfold increase of the 1630's nor by virtue of new arrivals. The increase was natural, the result of large families. Eight and ten children were not uncommon, and those of the eight or ten who survived childhood more than likely had eight or ten children each in their turn. Thus the 1,800 people of 1643 became almost 5,000 by 1675 and more than 10,000 by 1690.[40] New towns appeared, but they were settled from the older towns rather than by newcomers from England. Nauset (later named Eastham) on Cape Cod was settled from Plymouth and recognized as a town in 1651. In the early 1660's, Plymouth men settled Middleboro and Dartmouth. Duxbury men, to obtain farms for their children, purchased Indian lands which, in 1656, formed the town of Bridgewater. Rehoboth spawned Swansea, which was admitted as a town in 1667. Barnstable gave rise to Falmouth, which was recognized as a town in 1686, the same year that families from Scituate, Marshfield, Sand-

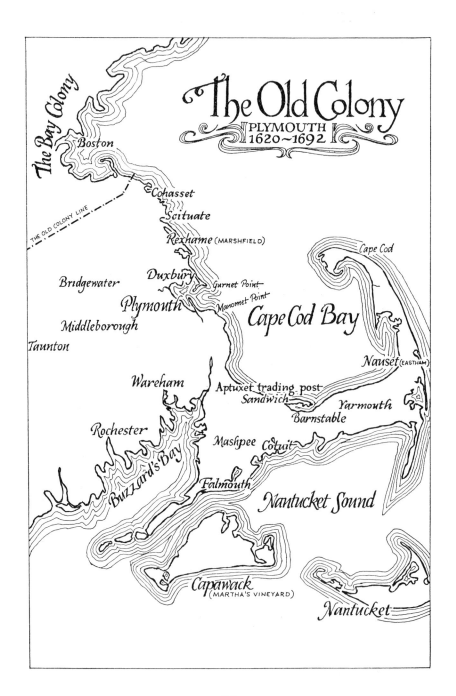

The Old Colony
PLYMOUTH
1620~1692

The Bay Colony

Boston

THE OLD COLONY LINE

Cohasset

Scituate

Rexhame (MARSHFIELD)

Bridgewater

Duxbury

Gurnet Point

Manomet Point

Plymouth

Cape Cod

Middleborough

Cape Cod Bay

Taunton

Nauset (EASTHAM)

Wareham

Aptuxet trading post

Sandwich

Yarmouth

Barnstable

Rochester

Mashpee

Cotuit

Buzzard's Bay

Falmouth

Nantucket Sound

Capawack
(MARTHA'S VINEYARD)

Nantucket

wich, and Plymouth settled along Buzzards Bay were recognized as the town of Rochester. The process was, in the seventeenth century, a never-ending one.

Historians have made much of the New England town (and Plymouth colony was, from the second decade, a collection of towns). They have most often written of the town in terms of a close grouping of houses neatly laid out around a town green or common and surrounded by the fields and meadows of the townsmen. Plymouth colony had none of this, however.[41] The towns were governmental and ecclesiastical units, handy for public and church affairs, no more. Geographically they were but collections of small villages and "naighbourhoods."[42] Dartmouth town, for example, was formed by combining the neighborhoods of Acushenah, Ponagausett, and Coaksett. Falmouth was a conglomerate of neighborhoods stretching from Woods Hole eastward along Vineyard Sound, neighborhoods which existed as far-flung parts of other towns from the early 1660's, when the area was called Saconessett, until Falmouth's organization as a town. (Notably, Falmouth's village green was not laid out until 1745.)[43] Plymouth itself, after the scattering of the 1630's, changed appearance. Where in the 1620's it had been a compact array of houses surrounded by small garden plots and, farther away from the center, slightly larger fields, it more and more straggled as its people "removed into Farmes in the Country." At mid-century the town embraced an area roughly sixteen miles long and nine miles wide. Eel River, Lakenham, "the little town," Jones River, Wellingsley, Rocky Nook, Plain Dealing, and the old village itself were all identifiable neighborhoods within the town; Middleboro, prior to its organization as a separate town, was just such a neighborhood, as were Sepecan, Sepecan Harbor, Wareham, and Mattapoisett on Buzzards Bay, prior to their being combined as the town of

Rochester. So wide-flung was the population that, in 1649, the town established a select committee of seven men to handle its affairs. "The distance of our habitations [one from the other] and sundry other Inconveniencies" made it difficult for the inhabitants to gather regularly at the town meeting.[44]

If the towns straggled, so too did the villages and neighborhoods within them. The smallest neighborhoods were no more than a few houses roughly grouped together, each house surrounded by its barns and outbuildings. The whole complex had a gray, weathered appearance, the buildings being constructed of unpainted sawed timbers and boards. The larger villages embraced a few more houses, one of them invariably a "public house" whose owner was licensed to sell wine and beer to the populace. That village from which the town took its name contained the meetinghouse where the inhabitants met for worship and public business, perhaps a few more houses and public houses than the surrounding villages, and the stores of two or three merchants. Outside the villages and neighborhoods—for settlement was not confined even to them—one would find scattered farmhouses, each boasting its own complex of barns, outbuildings, and fields.[45]

Within these communities, from the largest village to the smallest neighborhood, there was a general commitment to the soil. No clear distinction can be drawn between the farms and villages of Plymouth colony, or between farmers and villagers if one is distinguishing the farmer from the nonfarmer. For merchants and artisans, governors and clergymen were also farmers, and farmers were also innkeepers and handicrafters. The "better sort" who served as governors and magistrates or who ministered to the souls of the townspeople did not normally dirty their hands in the earth. But they owned land and were largely dependent upon it for their incomes. They rented land to tenants, as William Hanbury did the farm he purchased from John Brown, leasing it to Francis Goole with "a stock of six drawing beastes and two cowes and a horse, with plowes, yeokes, cheanes," and as Governor Bradford did "his farme by Jones River." Or they sent their servants to work the fields, as did the Reverend Charles Chauncy of Scituate. Chauncy, in 1647, owned a house, barn, outhouses, orchard, barnyard, and at least sixty-six acres.[46]

Others, not of the "better sort," more clearly merged farm and nonfarm activities. John Barnes of Plymouth, for example, is easily recognizable as a merchant. He was at various times a brewer, baker, innkeeper, and land speculator as well. But he was also a farmer. We can catch a glimpse of him in the records of the town and colony for the 1630's buying and selling cattle and mowing public meadow. In the early 1640's he was leasing land at Eel River to William Baker for fifty shillings a year, payable in money or corn, but presumably Barnes was working other land closer to his home himself. In 1651 he divided a part of his livestock among his children—four cows, two mares, two colts, and four sheep. His very death in 1671 was a result of a not untypical farm accident. Standing "before his barne dore in the street" he was "stroakeing or feeling of his bull" when the animal "suddenly turned about upon him" and gouged his thigh. Thirty-two hours later he was dead. The inventory of his estate, in addition to indicating his mercantile activities, reflects his closeness to the soil. A full complement of agricultural implements is listed, together with "Corne on the Ground" valued at two pounds sterling. And for all his earlier gifts to his children he still owned three cows, three steers, a calf, twenty-seven sheep, four mares, and a colt. (The guilty bull, unless masquerading as a steer, went unlisted.)[47] Gyles Rickard was a friend, neighbor, customer, and occasional drinking companion of Barnes. A weaver and sometime-innkeeper, he sent his sons digging in the tar pits around Plymouth and occasionally traded in competition with Barnes. But from the time of his arrival in the 1630's he amassed land here and there, and with his sons went out from his "house and orchyard and Barne" in the Wellingsley neighborhood of the town to plow, sow, reap, and mow. At the time of his death in 1684, weaver Rickard owned and farmed plots of nine acres, two acres, eighteen acres, seven acres of meadow, and held as speculation two fifty-acre plots.[48] Francis Combe of Middleboro was very much a farmer, working extensive acreage with his sons and two Indian servants at the time of his death, and renting out oxen to his neighbors. But he was also an innkeeper and miller.[49]

It is an axiom that men and women coming to establish a settlement in the New World first required a means of subsistence and secondly desired a way to profit. So it was at Plymouth. The first comers had from the very beginning looked to the land for their sustenance, bringing seed and tools with them, adopting momentarily, a strange communal agriculture and an even stranger Indian crop, but gradually turning toward ways and crops familiar from their English traditions. In the prosperity of the 1630's they found profit in the land, and Plymouth's economy was fixed. It would be an agricultural colony, its people farmers, its market Boston. Dispersed by 1643 from Yarmouth to Taunton, from Scituate to Rehoboth—none of the towns large, all straggling, many of them away from the water and its fish, and from the Indians and their furs, and all dependent economically upon the Bay capital—what other primary economic activity was open to the colony? True, an individual might combine his personal activities, working his land while serving the agricultural community as a merchant, or weaver, or innkeeper. But he who would be a cooper or a mason only and not a farmer, at least a part of the time, had best go to Boston to practice his trade! And some men did supplement their incomes with fish or fur, the commodities so important in the minds of the leaders of 1620. But who would eschew completely the secure profits of the land for the tenuous profits of such ventures?

The economy so fixed would prevail until 1692, when the Old Colony was merged with Massachusetts, surviving the depression of the early 1640's and the onset of the wheat blight or "blast," a fungus, perhaps black-stemmed rust, which periodically struck at the principal money crop after 1663. Only after 1692 does one find significant indication of other economic activity—shipbuilding on the North River, for example[50]—and even then the area that had been Plymouth colony would remain basically agricultural. The scene of James Wyatt of Taunton carting to his hay meadow on a hot July day would be as commonplace in the 1760's or 1860's as it was in the 1660's.

CHAPTER TWO

Wills and Inventories:
The Reconstructed Farm

WHAT OF LIFE IN THE OLD COLONY? What of everyday activity on the land, the tools used, and the crops raised? It is not easy to visualize, for the prosaic things of everyday life leave little imprint on the historical record. A number of English writers of the seventeenth century described farm practices current in England, although only incidentally and in the hopes of improving English farming. Plymouth farming was in the tradition of the English, and therefore much that was written of England applies to Plymouth as well. But farming in England differed from district to district, while the people of Plymouth came from many different districts. How did the varying agricultural traditions merge in the colony? What of the differences impressed on the English tradition by the New World? Corn, for example, was outside the English tradition, and English writers had nothing to say about its cultivation. And corn was only the most obvious difference.

Travelers in New England, colonial pamphleteers writing to induce new settlers to come, and diarists tell us something. Traveler John Josselyn, for example, jotted down weather signs: "Redness of the sky in the morning, is a token of winds, or rain or both," "mists . . . in the vallies . . . promise fair hot weather," "a little black cloud in the *North-West*" promises "a following storm." [1] We can, therefore, readily envision the Plymouth "goodman," on rising in the morning, casting a quick eye on the signs, then planning his day to accommodate their promise or warning. But travelers, pamphleteers, and diarists will not tell us all that we want to know. The diarist was generally hurried, and his entries were consequently scant, while the commonplace escaped both pamphleteer and traveler. Josselyn, describing New England to his English audience, would not describe the farmer sowing wheat or rye in his fields, for the scene was familiar to England and hence not worthy of the traveler's pen; unless unusual, the plow or harrow that the farmer used would go undescribed, for it was nothing but a common English plow or harrow. Indeed, the pamphleteers and travelers very often gave an erroneous impression about the land. The pamphleteers were prone to exaggerate such things as crop yields, while both pamphleteers and travelers tended to accent the unusual and neglect the familiar. Describing New England they would infrequently mention English grains because they were so ordinary. A word that English grains would grow and that the yield was good would suffice. But they would stress corn and pumpkins as oddities intriguing to their English readers. The historian relying solely on their works will, as a result, envision New England as a land of Indian corn and pumpkins, and the word picture he draws may well be far from the mark.

Vital clues to everyday life—and to the farm in particular—exist, however; clues directly relevant to the locality (as the English agricultural writers are not) and devoid of the exaggeration and partiality for the unusual which mark the pamphleteers and travelers. Town and colony records note grants of land to various individuals, while documents pertaining to the sale or lease of land frequently give extensive details and were always carefully preserved. Death, moreover, set in motion certain legal procedures: the probate of the will and inventory of the estate of the deceased, the appointment of an executor, and the periodic examination of the executor's activities by the colony's courts. Such procedures were all recorded and by and large the records remain to us. The wills and inventories are our best evidence of the everyday life of the past, for the items bequeathed and inventoried were not selected on the basis of their strangeness but on the basis of their value. From these records, augmented by the works of travelers, pamphleteers, diarists, and English agricultural writers, we can reconstruct the Plymouth farm.[2] In view of the pattern of development among the Old Colony's towns, however—the fact that, as we have seen, farm practices varied from town to town according to the age of the town—we must first establish an approximate time and place for our reconstruction. There was a general tendency to begin with cattle and shift to grain, a pattern which requires that our choice of time and place encompass both what the farmer was working away from and what he was working toward. Ideally, then, we place our reconstruction in Plymouth itself, the oldest town, at around 1650, when it was definitely committed to cultivation, yet not to the complete exclusion of cattle.

The "farmhouse," whether standing in the village or isolated in the countryside, was a crude affair by modern standards. At mid-century the most developed was a two-story frame structure built around a great brick chimney, a lean-to projecting from the rear in some cases. The outside was clapboarded but unpainted, although frequently the clapboarding was applied only to the front of the house; the sides and back, away from the view of passersby and visitors, were plain weatherboarding. Parlor and kitchen shared the first floor, being divided by the chimney and a small entrance hall. A narrow, winding staircase ascended from the entrance hall to the second floor, which boasted two bedchambers. Where there was a lean-to, it was normally divided into a general-purpose room and an "inner" room to the side, the latter sometimes used as a study, more often as an extra bedchamber. Occasionally three rooms shared the lean-to. A more typical house, perhaps, was but half the size—a single all-purpose room below, sometimes with a lean-to at the rear, and a chamber or merely a garret above. The light was dim within the house. Diamond-pane casement windows were common after 1640, replacing oil-paper, but they admitted little sunlight and, indeed, were normally covered with fabric in the winter to preserve warmth.[3]

Into such a structure the Plymouth family crowded itself and its possessions. Furniture was minimal, a few chests and presses to hold the family's clothes (there were no closets), a table, many chairs. But beds were everywhere—in parlor, kitchen, chambers, lean-to, even sometimes in the narrow space between the second-floor chamber walls and the roof—outsized and cumbersome bedsteads with blankets, rugs, and hangings to keep the occupants warm, trundle, or "truckle," beds, cots, cradles. And there was clutter. In part it was household clutter. In John Jenney's Plymouth village kitchen, for example, a globe and a few books shared space with "a kneadeing trough and cover," spinning wheel, and "3 old peecs a pistoll and a paire of bandeliers." But it was also farm clutter, the dwelling of necessity sheltering an array of produce and equipment. Jenney's kitchen was undoubtedly festooned with herbs and dried vegetables and fruits. In his parlor were stored "2 beere barrells & other lumber," the word signifying odds and ends. Ten pounds of feathers taken from Jenney's chickens and ducks waited to be stuffed into pillows and comforters in one bedchamber. In the other were stored a wheel, "2 old axes," "1 smal adds [adz] and other old iron," "2 old netts," "an old cartrope,"

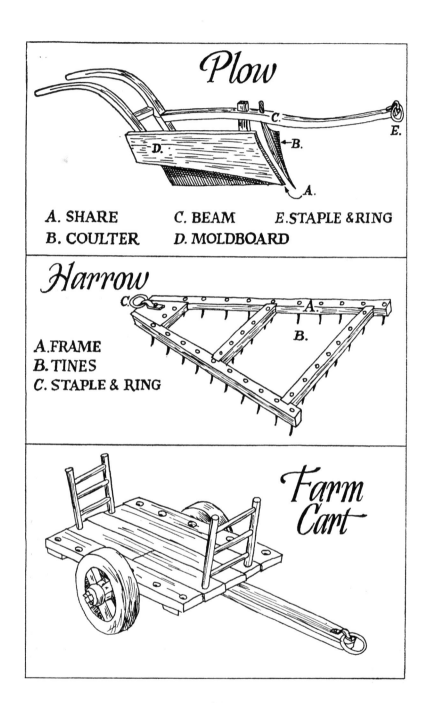

Plow

C.

E.

←B.

D.

A.

A. SHARE   C. BEAM   E. STAPLE & RING
B. COULTER   D. MOLDBOARD

Harrow

C.   A.

B.

A. FRAME
B. TINES
C. STAPLE & RING

Farm Cart

"2 jarrs tubs and old baskets and lumber," eighteen bushels of wheat and six bushels of barley.[4]

The clutter was outside as well. Around every house, frequently attached to the dwelling, was a variety of farm structures: dairy house, cowshed, slaughterhouse, chicken coop, and of course a barn. The barn was particularly crowded. A small structure, little bigger than the dwelling itself, the Plymouth barn was on the average no more than twenty to thirty feet long and fifteen to twenty feet wide. It was a stock barn, housing some of the livestock—oxen, dairy cows, horses, chickens nesting here and there if there was no chicken house. It was also a threshing barn, the man of the house and his sons somehow finding room for a threshing floor in season. And it was a storage barn. Threshed and unthreshed grain was tucked away wherever there was room. Some hay was stored in the barn, but the lack of room forced the farmer to store most of the hay in ricks in the barnyard, a rick being a carefully built stack of four or five loads of hay thatched with straw to keep off rain and snow. Some equipment was housed in the barn, too, although it would seem that a good bit was simply left "Without Doores," a recurring phrase in the inventories.

Like the furniture in the house, the farmer's equipment was minimal. The best equipped in Plymouth colony possessed but plow, harrow, and cart, together with fittings for each, and small tools—scythes, sickles, shovels, hay and dung forks, hoes. All of the equipment was crude and rough. Much of it was home-fabricated.[5]

In contemporary England a wide variety of plows existed. The "plaine plow" was hallowed by centuries of medieval use—a simple share attached to a wooden beam and moldboard and drawn through the earth by oxen. But there were also massive "Turnwrest" plows featuring double wheels and moldboards which could be turned from side to side at the end of a furrow so as to make the sod fall the same way coming and going, newly invented double plows cutting two parallel furrows, lightweight single-wheeled plows.[6] Plymouth inventories sometimes list simply "plow," giving no details, and we can assume that there perhaps were wheeled plows here and there. But most inventories list merely "ould share and Coulter," and this would indicate that the plain plow was most common, the coulter being a sharp cutter or knife which sliced through the soil in advance of the share, the share forming the furrow and throwing the soil back on a wooden moldboard, which turned it aside. Share and coulter were generally imported from England, attached to a home-hewn beam, which was in turn attached to the ox yoke by a chain fitted to an iron staple and ring at the tip of the beam, the whole fitted with a straight wooden moldboard and handles.[7]

The harrow was no more than a series of heavy beams linked together in the form of a figure "A," or triangle, or rectangle, into which were driven between twenty and forty forward-pointing teeth, or tines.[8] As was the plow, the harrow was largely home built. Iron teeth were brought from England (although occasionally hardwood teeth cut locally are mentioned in the inventories), fastened to a frame of the farmer's own contrivance, and linked to the oxen with a chain, normally the same chain as was used on the plow.

Not every farmer had a plow, well over half the extant inventories omitting mention of either plow or plow-irons. In every village, however, there were those who specialized in the heavy work of the farm, men like Henry Smith of Rehoboth, whose four oxen and two plows were available for hire and undoubtedly were busy throughout the spring season.[9] Fewer farmers were without a harrow, but a heavy branch dragged across the ground did light harrowing. Gervase Markham, an English writer of husbandry pam-

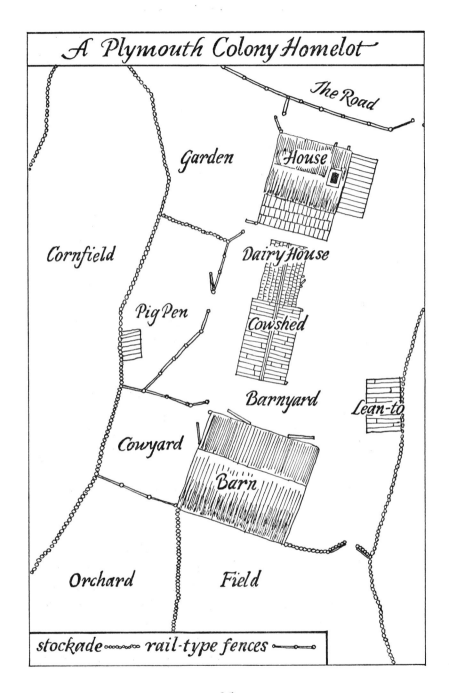

A Plymouth Colony Homelot

The Road

Garden

House

Cornfield

Dairy House

Pig Pen

Cowshed

Barnyard

Lean-to

Cowyard

Barn

Orchard

Field

stockade ∞∞∞ rail-type fences •—•—•

35

phlets, suggested this "new" practice to English farmers at mid-century.[10] For heavier work a neighbor's harrow could be hired.

Of the three pieces of major equipment, the cart—short-bodied and two-wheeled—was most basic. On it the farmer hauled his manure to the fields, his hay and grain to barn or barnyard, his produce to market, and his family to Sabbath meeting. The iron-rimmed wheels were most valuable and were frequently listed alone on Plymouth inventories. Some were partly home-hewn, the farmer cutting the wheels out of a hardwood log and mounting the rims on them. More often the rims were mounted on spoked wheels made by a local artisan. In either event the wheels turned on an axle made of a young tree stripped of bark and cut to length. Sundry accessories completed the cart: ladders mounted front and back to hold a load of hay; sideboards or rails; cart chains or ropes by which the oxen hauled the cart; sometimes a wooden cart tongue fastened to the front and attached directly to the oxen's yoke.[11]

House and barn formed the focal point of the Plymouth colony "homelot." But the homelot as a whole was a complex of yards—barnyard, cattleyard, pigpen, garden, and orchard. The barnyard was the vague area immediately around the barn and house, and like them it was cluttered. Equipment, hayricks, manure pile all competed for room. When the number of his cattle required it, the farmer built a cattleyard or "stall" adjoining the barnyard. Cattle which could not be accommodated in barn or cowshed were housed here during the winter. Perhaps some effort was made to shelter the cattle from the elements by erecting at least a roof over a part of the yard, but the major reason for the yard appears to have been to facilitate winter feeding. The yard, too, seems to have provided fertilizer for the fields. When, for example, Richard Chadwell lost a part of his cattleyard for a public road, the yard was considered "dunge ground" hence "a choise place," and Chadwell was allowed the right to "carry away att his pleasure, by cart or otherwise, soe much of the ground . . . as shalbee good for the manuring of his said land." [12]

As it had in old England the garden fell within the province of the women of the house, and what Thomas Tusser, the country poet of sixteenth-century England, had written of the English goodwife undoubtedly applied to her sister in Plymouth:

> In March and in April, from morning to night,
> in sowing and setting, good huswives delight:
> To have in a garden or other like plot,
> to trim up their house, and to furnish their pot. [13]

Idealizing the farmer's life, Tusser put equal weight on trimming up the house and furnishing the pot, but the pot was by far the more vital. "Goody" Hicks sowed and weeded her quarter-to-half-acre garden, manured and cultivated so assiduously, stole a moment here and there from housework to pluck up a trespassing weed or two, shooed away the blackbirds which constantly threatened, not for the garden's beauty but for its fruits. Her vegetables were the traditional English ones, and her leeks and onions, garlic, melons, English gourds and beans, radishes, carrots, cabbages, and artichokes ended up in dishes such as "bubble and squeak" (a combination of fried beef and boiled cabbage) and "succotash" (beef, chicken, field corn, and any and all vegetables thrown together and boiled). Few of the indigenous Indian plants were to be found in her garden. Corn, pumpkins, Indian gourds, and Indian beans were still field crops. Missing, too, were potatoes and tomatoes. Both had been introduced to England prior to colonization, but suspicious farmers and their wives everywhere looked askance at them.

37

Like all things new they were considered dangerous. Some said that if a man ate potatoes every day he would not live more than seven years.[14] Not until the end of the eighteenth century would potatoes be found in American gardens; tomatoes would not be accepted until the nineteenth century.

The goodwife's garden did boast herbs and flowers, however. The flowers undoubtedly added beauty and color. They were, nonetheless, one with the vegetables and herbs in the housewife's mind and were desired primarily for their usefulness. She did not even plant them apart in beds of their own but set violets, marigolds, and daffodils with the lowly onion, and intermixed daisies and lilies with the parsnips. Only the very aromatic did she treat with diffidence, planting roses, for example, in pots lest the aroma spread to the soil to the detriment of the rest of the garden.[15] The flowers, and aromatic herbs of all sorts, were a vital part of her housekeeping. The housewife sprinkled them in her linen and hung sachets in the doorways that the aroma might freshen the whole house. Culinary herbs seasoned her stews, salads, cakes, cooked fruits, and bread. Medicinal herbs were administered to her family. Some herbs had more than one use, and the goodwife knew them all. Dill, for example, was used in pickling and as a flavoring in salads. Boiled and drunk, it was considered excellent in easing swellings. Its seeds—some called them "meeting seeds"—were carried to Sabbath meetings by the children and nibbled during the long sermons; supposedly they dulled the senses and kept childish squirming at a minimum.[16]

As the garden fell within the women's province, the orchard fell to the men, and if the women stole moments now and again from housework to tend their vegetables and herbs, the men stole time to care for and undoubtedly admire the fruit trees. For of all things English, the fruit tree seems to have done best in New England soil. "Our fruit-

Trees prosper abundantly, *Apple-trees, Pear-trees, Quince-trees, Cherry-trees, Plum-trees, Barberry-trees,*" traveler Josselyn wrote; "the Countrey is replenished with fair and large Orchards." There is a tradition that seeds were carried on the *Mayflower* and planted the first year, and various travelers indicate that transporting the seeds was one method of bringing trees from England to America. "I have observed with admiration, that the Kernels sown . . . produce as fair and good fruit, without graffing, as the Tree from whence they were taken," Josselyn wrote.[17] Wild fruits of all sorts abounded, most of them similar to English fruits, although generally smaller and less tasty, and another tradition has the settlers domesticating these. But more than likely the orchards were started in the late 1630's and early 1640's from both seeds and saplings carefully carried across the ocean, buds or scions from the saplings being grafted onto stock grown from seed.[18]

Two land transfers in 1645 and 1646 respectively indicate that orchards were at that time both new and special. In the first the seller retained the right to take away "some fruit trees in the Orchard"—indicating that the trees were young and capable of being transplanted—"so that he leave" the buyer, John Churchwell, "thirty good fruit trees." In the second the seller retained all the fruit trees, promising to remove them from the land "in due time." Thomas Hill of Plymouth seems to have operated a short-lived nursery at Wellingsley Brook in the late 1630's, growing trees to sell to his neighbors. Having been granted land at the Brook in 1638, he sold it in 1641 to John Barnes, Barnes to receive fifty apple trees as well, twenty-five of which he was to choose "out of all the trees that the said Thomas Hill hath now unsold and thother 25 are to be chosen first John Barnes one and the said Thomas Hill another." Hill was to take away promptly what was left. Neighbor Francis

Goulder, apparently renting his land from George Russell, might have been another purchaser of Hill's trees, for in 1651 Russell sold a two-acre house lot to Gyles Rickard but provided that Rickard should pay Goulder fifteen shillings for "Certaine fruit trees" which Goulder had planted on the property. Presumably the trees were by that time too large to be transplanted.[19]

Barnes's fifty trees and Churchwell's thirty, both on relatively small holdings, indicate the size of the orchards. The trees were normally placed twenty to thirty feet apart. In England field crops or herbs and flowers were ordinarily planted between trees in an orchard, but this does not seem to have been the case in New England. Berry bushes, both indigenous and imported, were planted around the fences surrounding the orchards, however, and the ground between the trees might have been mowed for its hay, although some felt that grass too near the base of the trees would rob them of nourishment.[20]

In common with all New England the Plymouth men took great care with their trees. In late winter they spread "mucke" from the barnyard around the base of each tree, and pruned. In March and April grafting was done, for while there were no recognizable varieties except for the damson plum—a small, dark, purplish, sweet plum—the farmer continually experimented in an effort to improve the quantity and (to a lesser extent) quality of his fruit. In the summer the farmer watched for what Josselyn described as "meazels," a burning and scorching attributed to the sun, and for "lowsiness, when the woodpeckers job holes in the bark." The farmer had no remedy for the first, but for the second he bored a hole into "the main root" and poured in "a quantity of Brandie or Rhum," then closed the hole "with a pin made of the same tree." Apparently the brandy was to flavor the tree and so dissuade the woodpeckers from their work.

Late summer and fall brought the harvest. There was little need to pick the ripened fruit with care, for most of it ended in the cooking pot or cider press. A good shaking of each branch brought the fruit down to be picked up by the children and carried home. "The *Quinces, Cherries, Damsons* set the Dames a work," and soon "*Marmalad* and preserved *Damsons* is to be met with in every house." The apples were pressed in cider presses by those wealthy enough to have such a piece of equipment. Most Plymouth men, however, merely dropped the apples into a trough and pounded them with any convenient mallet, dipping out the juice and allowing it to ferment in barrels. Notably, the apple tree soon came to predominate, and one frequently finds the produce of an orchard given in terms of barrels of cider. But none in Plymouth seems to have outdone one Connecticut planter who boasted of five hundred barrels of good hard cider from his orchard in a single year.[21]

Beyond the homelot with its buildings, yards, garden, and orchard were the farmer's fields, in some cases contiguous to the homelot to form a farm in the modern sense, in others spread over several miles, a few acres here, a few more there.[22] Not all of the farmer's holdings were under cultivation. Many Old Colony men held unimproved land far removed from their homes and relatively inaccessible, buying it from other Englishmen, or from the Indians, or receiving it from the colony or town governments as part of the regular division of land which went on during the century. Eventually, they hoped, their sons might take up such land, or a new settlement would be formed near it, creating a market for the land so that it could be sold at a profit. But even of that land more immediate to the home (which we can consider the "farm"), large portions were untouched by the plow. Much was timberland, the tall trees affording the farmer winter wood and building material. By one estimate the average family needed fifteen cords of wood per winter, the equivalent of three-fifths of a standing acre. Marshland and some natural meadow were left uncultivated, the farmer merely cutting the grass once a year and making hay. Invariably the first fields brought under cultivation were laid out on natural meadows, Indian burnings, or on old Indian cornfields. Plymouth village itself had been established on land cleared by the Indians, the nearest timber being a quarter mile away. Settlers in later villages made use of similar clearings, Rehoboth, for example, being laid out on what was called "Seekonk Plain." [23] The stereotyped picture of the first settlers arduously clearing land and rooting up stumps is, therefore, an inaccurate one.

As the century progressed, however, the amount of improved land was steadily increased, individual farmers putting more and more of their land under cultivation, breaking the sod of the natural meadows, fencing, and planting. In time the inhabitants of the older villages had no more naturally cleared land and of necessity turned to timberland, probably making use first of that land from which they had been taking timber for firewood and building materials. More and more, too, new villages were settled on secondary clearings, and the inhabitants almost immediately turned to the woods, clearing the underbrush, felling trees, and removing stumps. Removing the underbrush was easily accomplished by burning or running cattle on the land, the cattle breaking down the brush and adding a natural fertilizer to the soil.[24] The trees were killed Indian-style, by girdling or burning their bases, then felled and burned where they lay that their ashes might fertilize the soil still more. Stump removal was undoubtedly the hardest work of the New World, the farmer digging around and under the roots, then using two, three, and four teams of oxen—his own and his neighbors'—to drag the stump out by brute force. In the eighteenth century some farmers eschewed stump removal. Discovering that they could plant in the ashes of the trees without plowing, they had no need to clear the roots to make way for the plow. But the men of the seventeenth century took no such shortcut, feeling themselves "obliged to stubb all Staddle" from newly cleared fields.[25]

What proportion of the Plymouth farmer's land was actually cultivated, and what did he plant on the land? For answers we must turn again to the inventories of the seventeenth century. Even in them the answers are not easily found, however, for the inventories do not list exact acreage. But they do, particularly in the 1640's and 1650's, list the quantities of various grains on hand at the time of the farmer's death, either directly in terms of bushels or indirectly in terms of value. Such entries tell us what crops were grown. Indian corn, wheat, and rye show up regularly in the inventories; oats, barley, and field peas less regularly. And the entries give us a clue from which we can deduce how much of each was sown and, consequently, how much of the farmer's total acreage was under cultivation. We need only select such inventories as allow us to assume that the grain on hand at the time of death and thus inventoried was the greater part of the produce of the farmer's fields and, additionally, to determine the yield per acre of each crop.

The yield per acre of Indian corn can be ascertained by using two inventory entries, one from July, 1641, the other from September of the same year: "14 acrees of Corne on the ground" valued at 30 pounds sterling; "Indian Corne 1000 hills old and new esteemed 50 bushels" valued at six pounds.[26] Given these two entries we can frame a problem in simple arithmetic: "If fourteen acres of Indian corn in the ground equals thirty pounds sterling and fifty bushels in the ground equals six pounds, how many bushels equal one acre?" The answer—the yield per acre—is eighteen.

We can compute the per-acre yield of rye in much the same fashion. Three inventory records of the 1640's give the value of acreages planted in rye; others give the value of so many bushels of rye in the barn.[27] From these entries, and taking into account the cost of harvesting and threshing the rye, we can compute the approximate yield at eight bushels per acre. Unfortunately, there are insufficient data to compute the yield of wheat, barley, oats, and field peas in this manner. But these crops are too important to be ignored, particularly wheat. Hence we must extrapolate from the known yield of rye.

Normally on light, sandy, and gravelly soil (the upland soil of the Old Colony) rye would yield considerably more than wheat. One might assume, therefore, that wheat yields were substantially less than those already computed for rye. But an anonymous writer of 1637 noted that in New England, while the soil was "precipitates of sand"—ideal for rye—"our rye likes it not." Even when the land was manured, the resulting improvement in yield did not "answer expectation." How does one pair the two facts? A letter drafted by the Massachusetts General Court in 1650 gives us the clue we need: "Much of our ground except newly broken up or Some choyce land extraordinary husbanded yields not above 6 or 8 bushels of wheate upon an Acre and some less and the like for Barle and pease. Rye and Indian yields some more." In other words, the wheat yield (six to eight bushels) was only slightly less than the rye yield (eight bushels by our previous determination). Yields of barley, peas, and oats—the last an assumption—were the same as for wheat.[28]

Applying these figures for yields to specific estates we can determine in a rough fashion the acreage planted in specific cases. Ephraim Hicks of Plymouth village, for example, died early in the spring of 1650, and the inventory of his estate was prepared in mid-March.[29] The inventory lists seventeen bushels of wheat, eleven bushels of rye, one bushel of peas, and an item "Corn uppon the ground" valued at seven pounds, five shillings, eight pence. (We can, recall, compute acreage when given the value by simply dividing the value by the going price per bushel, taking into account the cost of completing the crop and harvesting; this gives the number of bushels anticipated and hence, by utilizing our yield figure, the approximate acreage.) The grain in the barn was the product of the winter's threshing not yet passed on for debts and taxes, and represented the yield of the previous year (1649) less any home consumption. The early spring date of the inventory, given the fact that two plantings of Indian corn separated by several weeks were the rule in Plymouth colony, indicates that the "Corn uppon the ground" represented only half the crop planned for 1650. Hicks's holdings are also inventoried: sixteen acres, twelve fenced and four unfenced, in one plot; a six-acre field separated from the first; four other "parcells" of land of varying sizes—in all between thirty and thirty-five acres, plus "house and garden and barne." Assuming that his corn acreage in 1649 was the same as that intended in 1650 and adjusting for the home consumption of peas and rye (but not wheat, which, as a money crop, was too valuable to eat),[30] we can estimate that Hicks's farm in 1649 was broken down as follows: Indian corn, five and a half acres; wheat, two and a half acres; rye, two and a half acres; peas, one acre—the total under actual cultivation, eleven and a half acres, and the rest, a little over twenty acres, meadow, marsh, and uncleared timberland on which Hicks grazed his four oxen, one cow, one bull, and from which he obtained his firewood and winter's hay.

While Hicks's total holdings seem somewhat below average for the Old Colony, the breakdown of his farm was about the average breakdown. For when this procedure is followed in those instances where the extant inventories give sufficient data, the pattern of land usage which emerges follows that of this one example. In general, one-third of the average settler's land in an older village (Plymouth, Duxbury, Scituate) was under cultivation by mid-century, a proportion increased to about two-thirds by the end of the century. Elsewhere the proportion under cultivation decreased in direct proportion to the newness of the village. Everywhere, from mid-century on, the settler planted roughly half his cultivated land in Indian corn, presumably planting pumpkins, Indian beans, and gourds in the cornfields Indian-style, and the other half in traditional English crops. Among English grains wheat clearly predominated prior to the appearance of the wheat blast in the 1660's, with rye a not-too-close second. Wheat and rye share predominance thereafter. Field peas, barley, and oats were distinctly minor crops throughout the century, frequently neglected entirely. Two additional crops, flax and hemp, were officially encouraged by the colony government in order to lessen Plymouth's dependence upon imported cloth, but flax is only occasionally indicated in inventories, while hemp shows up even less frequently. The hop field was almost unknown in Plymouth.

The farmer's time was divided between his fields and his livestock. Almost every Plymouth inventory indicates stock of some sort: John Briggs (1641), three "melch Cowes," one heifer, one bullock, two bull calves, one sow and one "store pig," "three hens and some chickens"; Grace Granger (1648), "a young heifer"; William Lumkin (1670), three oxen, six cows, two calves, five pigs, one horse; James Bell (1677), one cow, two steers.[31] Frequently one-quarter of the total value of an estate was represented by livestock, occasionally as much as one-half. There is, however, a noticeable difference between the older and newer towns, the inventories of the newer towns showing a greater proportion of the total value in livestock than the older, together with a greater proportion of cattle among the livestock.

Neat stock—cows, steers, oxen—was by far the most common in all parts of the colony. No true breeds existed in the seventeenth century, but there were distinctive types associated with particular English districts and valued for different traits. Thus the long-horned cattle of Yorkshire, Derby, Lancashire, and Stafford—all black, with very large white horns tipped with black—were considered the most prolific breeder; the short, crooked-horned Lincolnshire cattle, pied with white and lanky in the body, were considered best as draft animals; the blood-red cattle of Somerset and Gloucester were especially valued for the quantity of milk produced. The description of the cattle divided in 1627 indicates that each of these types was brought to Plymouth very early. But it is improbable that the distinctions persisted. Indeed, in time a mottled red cattle—a merger of all these protobreeds plus Holland and possibly Swedish and Spanish stock from the Caribbean—would be looked upon as "native" New England cattle.[32]

If there was no clear distinction as to breed, there was a distinction as to care, one based upon that division between dry cattle and what can be termed "home stock," which we have already noted. The cattle sent abroad to graze semiwild on vacant land, for the most part destined for local or Boston butchers (although heifers and young bulls and steers were sometimes herded with the dry stock until brought into the village), tended to be rank and relatively unkempt, town and specific ownership being indicated only by a brand or cropped ear. The cattle kept at home—the milk cows, oxen, bulls, whose lot it was to provide the family with dairy products, labor, and calves—were carefully tended and as well fed as possible. In a sense such animals were part of the family to which they belonged, children being given calves to raise, wills specifically dividing animals among the children, and familiar names reflecting the animals' individuality—Thomas Bliss's oxen "Quick" and "Benbo," "Spark" and "Swad," his heifer "Traveller" and cow "Damson," for example.[33] John Barnes standing before his barn door "stroakeing or feeling of his bull" was undoubtedly a familiar scene.

Horses were less common than neat cattle. Again, there was no distinguishable breed. The old English black, or "Great horse," had been carefully bred from stallions imported from all over Europe to carry warriors, and in the sixteenth and seventeenth centuries such horses had been introduced into the barnyard to breed with what one writer has called "the wretched little animals" which the farmers used.[34] But the process of improving the farm horse had not gone far. Plymouth's horses—used for riding and sometimes joined with oxen to form a team—were undoubtedly more "wretched" than "great." The raising of sheep was periodically encouraged by the colony government but with only limited results, for not one in fifteen Plymouth inventories lists them. Goats are somewhat more frequently found. The former were valued for their wool and mutton, the latter for their milk. Swine were far more common than either, being more useful than the goats and having a far easier time in the rough country of America than the sheep. Indeed, the number of swine might well have equaled the number of cattle. Long and large-bodied with thick thighs and short legs, the Plymouth pigs were of almost any color from white through sand to pied and all black, although the last was considered a sickly type. And while their meat was somewhat on the lean side, they were cheap and easy to raise. Corn and alewives were relatively inexpensive feed for them, while

a sow farrowed three times a year and twelve to sixteen pig-
lets were common in a litter.[35] They were troublesome, however. Constantly escaping from their pens, they made straight
for the nearest cornfield or garden to the dismay of the
owners of the pigs, who were responsible for damages, and
the owners of the crops in which the errant pigs rooted.
Hence the laws were stringent. Swine had to be penned,
yoked, and ringed—the yokes to prevent their squirming
through fences, the rings that they might be caught the
easier if they did escape.[36]

The barnyard abounded with small animals, too. Cats, the
familar tabbies of today, were kept as protection against
rodents. Dogs were common. And there was poultry: ducks,
turkeys occasionally, and chickens—the dunghill fowl,
middle-sized, every variety of color, and not a particularly
good layer, but the best to be had at the time.[37]

All the animals about the barnyard had to be cared for,
fed, milked, and watered—the laborious, time-consuming
daily chores familiar to only a few in our modern urban
society. Men, women, and children shared these tasks. In
England, milkmaids undertook the feeding of poultry,
gathering eggs, and milking, so undoubtedly these tasks
fell to the girls of the Plymouth family, who milked
regularly around six in the morning and six at night. The
yield was not great. Two gallons at a milking was considered
extraordinary, while but one gallon was not at all unusual.
None tried for a better yield, however. Even in England
those attempting breed improvements were generally more
concerned with the size of the animal than the quantity of
milk. Men and boys did the heavy work of pasturing the
larger animals or, in winter, feeding them, cleaning the
stalls in the barn, and, of course, late in the fall, the slaugh-
tering.[38]

The man of the family, his older sons, and possibly a

servant or two cared for the fields. The work depended upon the season. Plowing began in March as the ground softened. With his crude plow and slow-moving oxen the farmer could go through no more than an acre a day. Harrowing followed at a faster pace. Ground to be planted in English grains was plowed and harrowed in its entirety. That to be planted in Indian corn was plowed only partially, the farmer merging English and Indian methods. Single furrows were plowed about six feet apart, lengthways and crossways in the field, to form a gridiron pattern, the points where the furrows crossed being the equivalent of the Indian "hills." From mid-March to mid-May was planting time.[39] In the cornfield the farmer cast the seed corn onto the hills created by his plow and covered the seed with a hoe or by plowing other furrows so that the sods would fall atop the hills. Two plantings were normal, the farmer adding (Indian-style) bean, gourd, and pumpkin seeds to his hills as the corn shoots appeared. Wheat and rye had at first been planted in the fall to mature in late spring—the traditional English planting—but the harder New England winter tended to kill the seed, and the farmers switched very early to spring varieties, sowing wheat and rye, together with peas, barley, and oats, broadcast in April, and harrowing lightly to cover the seed.[40]

Between sowing and harvesting there was more work to be done. The assiduous cultivation of the corn by the Indian women was not emulated by the English. They hoed in May, chopping the weeds from the hills that the shoots would not be crowded out. But then the farmer let the field of Indian corn go until the weeds began to "overtop" the young corn, at that time plowing between his original furrows (being careful not to destroy the gourd and pumpkin runners), turning the weeds under, and at the same time throwing dirt against the cornstalks so that the summer storms would not knock them down.[41] The grainfields in the first weeks after planting had to be protected against the same blackbirds that threatened the goodwife's garden. Bounties were offered by various towns for killing the birds. More effective were the boys who were sometimes stationed in the fields, the scarecrows erected, and the lines, strung across the fields, to which were attached fluttering cloths. There were other pests, too— flocks of passenger pigeons to be scared away, caterpillars, mice, and periodic infestations of locusts. In June a desultory weeding of the grainfields was attempted, the farmer and his helpers pulling up the rankest of the weeds; with the fields sown helter-skelter as they were, little more could be done.

July and August were the haying months. The grass was cut with a long-handled scythe, about an acre a day, and allowed to lie where it fell, the farmer coming two or three times to turn the grass to let the sun cure it. More than at any other time he watched the weather signs, for an untimely rain might undo much work. Fully cured, the hay was carted to the barnyard and, for the most part, formed into ricks. The cartload was about one ton and represented the yield of an acre of meadow or a half acre of marsh; four to five loads made up a rick, and the Plymouth barnyard might boast as many as three or four ricks when the haying was over, the product of the farmer's own land and whatever public land (including roadsides) his town allowed him to mow.[42]

Harvest began in August and early September in the grainfields. Wheat, rye, and peas were cut with a hook-shaped, short-handled sickle—hard, backbreaking work; barley and oats were cut with a scythe to which was attached a cradle. Once cut, all but the peas (which were handled much like hay) were tied in sheaves and piled into shocks to await carting to the barn. A good reaper could cut about an acre a day, eight to ten shocks of twelve sheaves each. The cornfields were turned to in September—sometimes as late as

October—the ears, beans, gourds, and pumpkins picked first and stored away, then the stalks cut down for winter fodder for the animals. Fall plowing and sowing followed the harvest before the turn to spring wheat and rye. In the eighteenth century, fall planting returned to some extent, the farmers turning back to winter wheat as a result of the blast, for the rust normally struck in midsummer, and the early maturing winter wheat proved somewhat immune.[43]

There was no respite from work in cold weather. Winter was a time for repairing equipment, spreading manure on the fields, felling timber, and cutting firewood to season by the following winter. It was the threshing time, too. On not too cold days, when the great double doors of the barn could be opened for fresh air, a threshing floor would be cleared, the sheaves dropped down from their resting place in the rafters, untied, and the grain beaten from the straw. Grain and chaff were separated by winnowing, either using "corn (*i.e.* English grain) fans" to toss the mixture into the air so that the grain would come straight down and the chaff be blown to the side, or merely tossing the mixture back and forth across the floor, the heavier grain going to the other side, the chaff falling in the middle. Either way was inefficient, the finished grain containing a goodly proportion of "trash." The threshing was hard, dirty work. And it was slow, only a few bushels a day.[44] Husking and stripping the kernels from the corn were less difficult. Indeed, the work seems to have been given over to the young people of the neighborhood for a social gathering, one traveler reporting that "husking of *Indian-Corn,* is as good sport for the Amorous *Wag-tailes* in *New-England,* as *Maying* amongst us is for our forward Youths and Wenches." [45]

Despite all the work the farmer's yields were meager. Grain yields of six, eight, and ten bushels per acre and corn yields of eighteen are abysmally low in twentieth-century terms. More important, the yields were low even in terms of seventeenth-century England. Sir Hugh Plat, writing in 1601 of English husbandry, commented that wheat of thirty-two bushels per acre would content the ordinary farmer, that many English farmers harvested forty-eight bushels, and a few, fifty-six. Undoubtedly he was exaggerating, but Edward Maxey, who was expounding a new way to plant grain and consequently understated the yield obtained by traditional methods, such as those used in Plymouth, wrote of yields of sixteen to twenty bushels per acre.[46] The true figure, although varying from one area to another in old England, was somewhere between the two. But Plymouth's yields were well below even Maxey's understated figure.[47] They actually seemed to have dropped to the level of thirteenth- and fourteenth-century England![48]

How does one account for this decline in yield? Was the soil of New England so poor? The earliest commentators on New England had not thought so. "I never came in a more goodly Country in all my life . . . for every thing that is heere eyther sowne or planted prospereth far better then in old England," one has written, while another spoke of "rich and fat" ground.[49] The land, however, did not live up to these promises. It was "like your woodland in England, best at first, yet afterwards grows more barren." [50] Even those who claimed the most for it—William Wood, for example, who promised impossible yields of thirty and forty bushels per acre in the 1630's—obliquely hinted at the worst, writing that "it is neyther impossible nor much improbable, that upon improvements the soile may be as good in time as *England*." An observer later in the century was more direct. The "fruitefullnesse [of the soil] is more beholding to the influences of the heavens, advantages of the seasonable skill and industry of the husbandmen, then the strength of its own temper." [51] In truth, the sandy, acid, easily leached soil of the Plymouth area was ill-suited to agriculture.

Soil alone might account for poor yields. But the attitudes of Plymouth farmers played a part too. On the one hand, they were hardworking and conscientious; their agricultural calendar was filled with activity. On the other, however, they disdained certain arduous English farm practices. Difficult but desirable crops such as flax, hemp, and hops were rejected. No field was allowed to lie fallow as in England, and the three or four plowings of the fallow were, of course, ignored. Cross-plowing of the grainfields as practiced in England—a second plowing at right angles to the first—and crop rotation were the exceptions, not the rule. Gleaning— the practice of going through a grainfield after the reapers to pick up every stray kernel—was unpracticed. No thought was given to draining, trenching, and ridging. Indeed, the Plymouth farmer resorted to the easiest methods at hand, the free grazing of a large part of his cattle, for example; the halfway adoption of Indian agriculture in which he abandoned both the energetic weeding of the Indian women and the full plowing of the English tradition.

Moreover, England was experiencing—and Plymouth largely ignoring—the prelude to the English agricultural revolution of the next century. In England some men were, as never before, giving thought to the land and its improvement. Earlier English writers on husbandry had merely translated classical expositions of little practical value or, like Thomas Tusser in the sixteenth century, simply described in almanac-fashion the most profitable activities of a given season:

> Green rye in September, when timely thou hast,
> October for wheat-sowing calleth as fast;
> If weather will suffer, this counsel I give,
> leave sowing of wheat, before Hallowmas eve.[52]

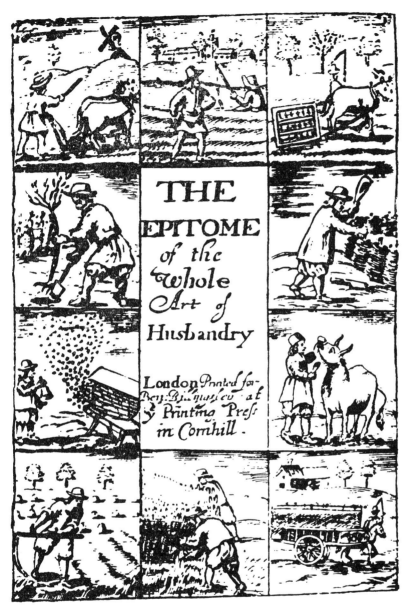

English farming scenes from Joseph Balgrave's *Epitome of the Whole Art of Husbandry* (1669). (Courtesy, Museum of English Rural Life, University of Reading, England)

Tusser, too, had idealized the farm and farmer, subscribing, for example, to the old maxim that "the best donge for the land is its Master's foot walking over it." But the new breed of writers in the seventeenth century idealized less and advised more: Gervase Markham, William Lawson, John Worlidge. Any one of them might have been cruel enough to suggest that if Tusser had relied less on the master's foot and more on dung he would not have died a pauper, his bones consigned to St. Mildred's Poultry. The difference between Tusser and those who followed him can be summed up with reference to "Husbandly Furniture," or equipment. Tusser was content to list equipment; Markham described in great detail how to construct and better it.[53]

The new writers were advocating agricultural improvements.[54] Sir Hugh Plat and Edward Maxey as early as 1600 and 1601 were arguing against the time-honored broadcast method of sowing grain—the slow traversing of the field by the farmer, seed sack slung around his neck, his hand constantly in motion casting the seed to right and left. It was picturesque, and novelists such as Knut Hamsun (in his *Growth of the Soil*) have exploited that quality. But it was uneconomic, a fact that Maxey particularly pointed out. By carefully planting the seed in orderly rows one could sow an acre with but half a bushel to the older method's two-and-a-half bushels. Various devices were tried to facilitate such ordered seeding, including a prototype of a modern seed drill, which, alas, could not be brought to work.[55] Maxey, Markham, and others suggested spring sowings of wheat and rye to supplement the traditional winter wheat planted in the autumn. Still others suggested treating the seeds to make them less appetizing to birds. Improved livestock breeding was recommended by many writers. John Evelyn turned his attention to soil analysis in an attempt to formulate exact rules by which a given type of soil might

NEW ADDITIONS to the Epitome of the Art of Husbandry Sold by B.Billingsley at the Printing Press in Cornhill

English farming scenes from Joseph Balgrave's *New Additions to the Epitome of the Art of Husbandry* (1669). (Courtesy, Museum of English Rural Life, University of Reading, England)

be improved by a given fertilizer. Markham and, particularly, Lawson devoted long pages to the improvement of gardening and orchard practices. Much was written of new crops, too, particularly root crops and artificial grasses such as clover. Men like Samuel Hartlib and Robert Boyle sought to amass information on farm practices and products throughout England and the whole world, hoping to systematize what they collected for the general advancement of England's farming. Hartlib's work resulted in his *Compleat Husband-Man* and a dozen-odd other works which he either authored himself or "borrowed" from other authors. Boyle enlisted the Royal Society in the effort, preparing a list of questions to be answered by travelers from their observations in England or abroad. He himself solicited information from those with specialized knowledge—John Winthrop, Jr., of Connecticut, for example, from whom he sought information on Indian corn.[56] John Houghton, another member of the Royal Society, published for a brief period an agricultural "newspaper," *Letters for the Improvement of Husbandry and Trade*. An early climax to all these efforts was a suggestion to establish an agricultural college in England.[57]

Little of this had an effect in Plymouth colony, or anywhere in New England. Historian Robert R. Walcott has suggested that the reason was that the New England farmer had no time for experimentation: "Of what use to him was the advice of Worlidge and Markham and the other English theorists, when what little time and labor he could spare must go toward clearing another acre or two for the future?" And besides, "in a certain sense, clearing land was [itself] an improvement." [58] Perhaps. But it hardly seems that the average Plymouth farmer made a conscious decision to set aside the advice of the theorists. In isolated Plymouth the average man undoubtedly did not read the agricultural books so avidly turned out by English writers. Only once in two hundred inventories collected from all the villages of the Old Colony is there a mention of an agricultural handbook of any sort, *Goades Husbandry*, as listed among the books belonging to Doctor Samuel Fuller in 1633. "Goades" was either a misreading for Godfridus, and the book the relatively useless *Knowledge of Things Unknowne with the Husbandmans Practise* or a more accurate reading of Thomas Goad's *The Doleful Even Song* and hardly useful to the good doctor.[59] There might well have been other pamphlets in New Plymouth, but the all-too-frequent inventory notation "parcel of ould books" hides them from us if they existed.

Some of the new information did seep into the colony, probably by word of mouth from a few leaders, and contrary to Walcott, the Plymouth farmer adopted what he found immediately useful. When the seed of winter wheat failed to withstand the New England cold the farmers turned to the spring wheat which the theoreticians were advocating. The wild grasses of New England posed a problem. Although plentiful and, during the summer and fall, rich feed for cattle, the New World grasses lacked nourishment when turned into hay. As a result the winter-fed cattle were badly nourished, and their diet of necessity was supplemented by corn. What was termed "English grass" was imported by some to rectify the situation. This may well have been nothing more than unwinnowed chaff gathered from English haymows and stacks and sprinkled on New England meadows, the unimproved English grass improving that of the New World. But the careful preparation of a seedbed for new grasses which one finds here and there, and the appearance of clover in New England—a grass urged on old England by the reformers—suggests that at least some were going farther in pursuit of an improved hay.[60]

The abandonment in Plymouth of traditional English

practices—the fallow, cross-plowing, gleaning—and the ignoring of most of the reforms advocated by the agricultural writers give an aura of backwardness to the Plymouth farmer when viewed through English eyes. Traveler Edward Ward reflects this in the extreme in his narrative of a *Trip to New-England with a Character of the Country and People:* "One Husband-man in *England,* will do more Labour in a Day, then a *New-England* Planter will be at the pains to do in a Week." [61] In reality, however, the Plymouth husbandman was neither ahead of nor behind his English brother, but proceeding along a different path.

England was moving toward intensive agriculture; the Plymouth settlers, and others all along the American coast, were at least psychologically tending toward extensive agriculture.[62] They were aspiring Englishmen and cast their aspirations in terms of land. The individual might not have broad acres in actuality. His farm might be no more than Hicks's thirty to thirty-five acres. But he lived in a land where he could at least envision limitless expansion, and more often than not he sought to add to his farm a variety of interests or claims in areas in the process of being opened up, intending to hold the new lands for speculation or as an inheritance for his sons. His obsession with land crops up in the judicial records, where cases of trespass and duplicate claims to the same land occur on just about every page. It dominates town records, page after page being devoted to applications for and grants of land. And in the colony records themselves one finds the regular creation of new towns, the establishment of land reserves for older settlers or their progeny, and the reflection of constant contention over the land as towns argued as to their boundaries, or one group within the colony pressed for favored treatment in regard to land allocations, frequently at the expense of some other group.

Yet the obsession with the land did not include—indeed, it tended to preclude—an intense and educated desire to exert great labor on the land. Why, the men of Plymouth might have asked, should we put so much effort into one small plot when there is so much virgin land to be had so cheaply?—an attitude reflected by William Wood when he wrote that "if any man doubt the goodness of the ground, let him comfort himself with the cheapness of it." [63] Moreover, living in a society lacking clear occupational differentiation, the men of Plymouth were often involved in activities additional to those associated with agriculture. Why, they might have asked themselves, put so much energy into farming when there are so many other ways to wealth and position? The net result was that they sought always a maximum of yield with a minimum of effort, abjuring maximum effort which might bring greater yield. They fertilized their fields so diligently, spreading manure on them, burning the brush and turning the ashes under with plows, because ash and manure were at hand and the poor quality of the soil was apparent to all. They accepted the spring wheat and experimented with the improved grasses offered by the English agricultural writers because the effort was small and the return great. Similarly, they combined English and Indian methods for growing corn—with crosshatched plowing the result—because the effort was decreased with no apparent loss of yield. True, their subsistence came from cultivating the soil. Their fields, orchards, gardens, and cattle supplied their tables. Their grain and cattle paid for those items which they could not produce for themselves. True, too, that the number of acres which could actually be farmed by the average family with the equipment available was a constant (and was normally only a portion of the family's total acreage). The average Plymouth farmer, without servants, could cultivate at most about twenty-five acres. The level of subsistence, therefore, clearly depended upon the intensiveness of the family's farming rather than the amount of land held. That the men of Plymouth ignored this logic, that they seemingly valued land in and of itself far more than they valued the produce of the land (and hence were content with low yields while contentious for more land) reflects not to their discredit but to their position as harbingers. They were in the mainstream of a developing American agriculture.

CHAPTER THREE

Epilogue

LIFE IN THE OLD COLONY was at every level farm life. The economy was based upon the products of the colony's soil. Farm families—in the sense of families whose sole activity was agricultural—predominated in the population. Artisans, merchants, innkeepers, magistrates, and ministers were, however, involved with the land as well, both directly, through their own personal interests and activities (albeit part-time), and indirectly, by virtue of the nature of the economy within which they lived. This total commitment to the soil is the key to a fundamental and often observed factor in the Old Colony's story. Plymouth was, until its merger with Massachusetts in 1692, a backwater, its people quiet and basically conservative, seldom rising above the ordinary round of daily work. Literature, art, music, and the drama had scant part in their lives, and they contributed little that was unique but the story of their first years to either the culture or tradition of American life.[1] One historian has attributed this to the religious origins and pursuits of the settlers.[2] But this seems hardly the case. Relatively few of Plymouth's first people stemmed from Leyden origins; the greater number were Londoners sent over by the merchant backers. Those who came during the second decade were from almost every part of England and traveled the route from England directly to Plymouth—or, more frequently, to Massachusetts Bay, then south to the Old Colony—out of every conceivable motivation. Again, one can hardly describe nearby Boston, equally religious in its origins and pursuits, in the same tones as Plymouth. The quiet backwardness of Plymouth is better accounted for by the rural setting of the colony and the rural pursuits of its people.

Plymouth's total commitment to agriculture is, moreover, a key to an almost traditional attitude on the part of historians toward the Old Colony. Historians have largely concerned themselves with contention and the clash of interests, with debtors versus creditors, farm interests versus commercial interests, backcountry versus the older, more urbane areas, intellectual contention. Plymouth had little of this. The colony's controversies were relatively minor and readily resolved; basic conflicts were none at all. The difference between older and newer villages was small, merely a different position in the same agricultural progression through which all Plymouth's villages were going. There was even less to differentiate the merchant from the farmer. And given the credit economy all men were debtors to someone else, and all men creditors.

With little of what interested them to be found in Plymouth, historians have tended to ignore it. The *Mayflower* and the earliest years—encompassing the high drama of beginnings and struggle—together with the various "firsts" which can be accounted to Plymouth, have had their due. But the "flapdoodle about the *Mayflower* and the Pilgrim fathers," as Samuel Eliot Morison has written, is followed by a rush "to the lush if somewhat sulphurous fields of Massachusetts Bay, Connecticut, and New Haven; to Rhode Island, popular today because of her fancied contribution to democracy." [3] Plymouth during the more than half century between the end of her first decade and the end of the colony's independent existence has usually been dismissed as a land of dull politics, of a colorless succession of governors dealing reasonably well with relatively small crises stimulated from outside the colony rather than from within.[4]

One can suggest that the fault is not in Plymouth but in historians. Change, the historian's prime concern, is not exclusively the product of jarring clashes; it comes at times, perhaps more often than not, like Carl Sandburg's fog, "on little cat feet," the slow product of consensus. Certainly this is the case with social change. One sees it in regard to agriculture: the cultural baggage of the settlers included agricultural methods and attitudes which slowly, over time, without great contention, changed. And one can envision the same slow change in countless other areas of human activity and organization: the family, certainly; the church; attitudes toward the community and state. Plymouth, confined in size and time—and therefore subject to a control absent in, for example, the much larger Massachusetts Bay—with a full range of materials readily available to the historian, is ideal for the empiric exploration of the dynamics of change and of the actual changes which brought Englishmen in the seventeenth century partway along the road to becoming Americans.[5] The very absence of basic conflict is an asset, for conflict can be an extraneous factor given more than deserved weight by the very fact of its occurrence. Approached for such purposes by historians less interested in extraordinary contention and more interested in ordinary people, the Old Colony—the quiet backwater of New England—will yield stories great in implication.

Appendix

THREE REPRESENTATIVE INVENTORIES

THE THREE INVENTORIES reproduced here afford a glimpse into the everyday lives of Plymouth's people. Each has been chosen for a purpose. Joseph Holloway of Sandwich, with personal property at the time of his death worth over 200 pounds sterling, was far better off than the average man in Plymouth, but the inventory of his estate shows the variety of agricultural implements utilized in the Old Colony. Francis Street of Taunton was the average man of Plymouth colony around mid-century, his estate amounting to just over 40 pounds in personal property and 70 pounds in real property. William Lumkin of Yarmouth, somewhat better off, was both farmer and weaver, as the mixture of farm and weaving implements in the inventory indicates. The dates are those of the preparation of the inventories.

JOSEPH HOLLOWAY
(*December 1647*)

	[*li*	*s*	*d*]
his wearing aparell and mony in his purse	42	0	0
one great chist 2 small chists 2 boxes one case of botels	1	4	0
4 pewter platers 4 basons 2 drinking pots and divers Smalle peeces of pewter more	1	3	0
4 firkins and one littell pot all full of buter	4	14	0
twelve Cheesses		4	0

Appendix

	li	s	d
a great peece of porke Som smale peesses and 60 *li* of beefe and som lard and som talow	1	15	0
2 barells one churne 2 tubbs		10	0
six peeces of taned lether and 7 scins of whit lether	1	16	0
som Sheeps woole and som coten woolle and Som yarne	1	0	0
in peassen	4	0	0
in Indian corn	3	0	0
in barly	1	6	0
in wheat	1	6	0
in hay	2	10	0
3 fether beads 2 bolsters 4 pilows 2 Rugges 2 coverlids 5 blankits 3 sheets and five plowbeers [pillowcases]	7	0	0
4 oxen	24	0	0
2 steers and an hayfer that bee goeing on 2 year ould	6	0	0
five calves	4	0	0
6 cowes	27	10	0
one bull	3	0	0
one Mare and a yeare ould coult	14	0	0
4 young shots [shoats]	1	10	0
one wayne [cart] 2 yokes and 3 chaynes	2	0	0
an Adventure [investment] in the [ship] adventure	5	5	0
2 cow hydes	1	0	0
8 yards and an halfe of carsy [jersey]	3	0	0
24 yards of stufe	33	5	0
one great brasse pan 4 kittels 3 smale pans one scellit	4	10	0
4 Iron pots one payer of pot hanggers and 2 pair of pothooks	1	15	0
one yard of cloth		7	0
one fouling peece one Muskat one sword one payer of bandeleers som powlder and shot	2	5	0

	[*li*	*s*	*d*]
one silver spoone		8	o
one hogshead of mault wanting a bushell	1	4	o
one twibill [double-headed ax] 3 axes 8 augers 3 chissills and 3 or 4 smale things	1	3	o
2 sithes and one Sned [a pruning tool]		4	o
one square 4 playnes one spokshave one drawing-knife one croscut Saw one hand Saw		18	o
one harow with 37 teeth one coulter and one share		13	o
4 Iron wedges 1 adds one ould payer of pinsons [pincers] one broken hamer 4 ould fyeles		10	o
3 Reape hooks 2 payer of compasses one gimblit		2	o
3 payer of ould [fiber] cards 2 meales sives and one new botom for a sive		5	o
2 pewter botles one litle lether botell and one glase botle and one Skumer [skimmer]		4	o
one warming pan and one peece of ould brase		6	o
one milke ladder one brush one dish one spoon		3	o
five Round Kimnils [tubs]		6	o
boards and Slabse		11	o
2 bedsteds 2 chairs 2 stooles		7	o
som ould Iron one how one spade one peale [oven or fire shovel] one smothing Iron		7	o
12 pound of coten woole to be Receved		11	o
2 payles		2	o
1 cheessprese 2 cheesfats [vats] one childs cradell		6	o
one chamberpot one brushe one emty ferkin a peece of a cartrope one payer of hooks and a stapell for a yoke one ould payer of bellows one payer of broken tonges		7	o

68

	[*li*	*s*	*d*]
the manure one litle earthen pot one pitch-fork one payer of tinnes for a fork one frying pan		9	0
dew from Mr leveridge		15	0
dew from gorg Allin	3	0	0
dew from Willi Gifford		3	4
2 bushells of wheat dew from Thomas dexter			
These debts are Judged desperate which are foloing			
dew from Mathew Alin of harford	1	0	0
dew from John hardy of Salem	2	0	0
dew from Richard foster		12	0
6 trenchers five or six Indian baskits and divers smale things not worth the writing downe and all other things that are for-goten	1	0	0
4 peecses of linnin cloth valued at 4 shilli			
	205	6	10

but ther is 12 *li* and 12*s* in desperate debts

Ther is two years and an half servis in a boy
but hee is a very bad servant

things forgoten
  half a bushell of wheat dew from Gorg
    bewitt
  one bushell of Indian dew from Thomas
    gibbs
  In childbead linnin and other linnin not
    valewed

FRANCIS STREET
(*June 1665*)

	[*li*	*s*	*d*]
Imprimis his wearinge apparell	5	0	0
Item one Iron pott & a Iron kettell	1	0	0
Item one brasse pott & skellet		6	0
Item in pewter		6	0
Item 2 books		15	0
Item a horse and saddell	6	0	0
Item a 3 yere olde stere	4	0	0
Item 5 cattell more	12	5	0
Item 6 swine	5	0	0
Item a sword and belt		10	0
Item a plow and other winkinge Implemts		16	0
Item in timber vessell chasse & chayre [in wooden utensils, boxes, and chairs]	1	5	0
Item 2 pott hangers, one fire shovell & hoocks		8	0
Item in severall smale things & some wollen yearne & bags not prissed [priced]	1	10	0
Item in debts due	2	18	0
	41	19	0
for his house & lands we value at	70	0	0

WILLIAM LUMKIN
(*January 1671*)

	[*li*	*s*	*d*]
and first his clothing	4	0	6
one gould ring	1	0	0
Tabble linnen	1	2	0
pillo-beears		15	6
in sheets	3	16	0
one Carpit		10	0
one great brush		1	6
The bed in the parlor	5	18	0

Appendix

	[*li*	*s*	*d*]
The bed Steed		5	0
One chect 1 *li.* one chest & box 1 *li*	2	0	0
Yarne 12*s:* a table 10*s:* 2 Chaires & Cushins 4*s*	1	6	0
andirons & tongs		13	0
in the Citching: the bed & bedding	6	3	0
a warming pan		14	0
in peutar	2	11	0
a drinking Cup edge with silver		3	0
2 Earthen dishes 1*s:* spoons 1*s:* In a chare 1*s* 6*d,*		3	6
Trais 3*s.* pailes 2*s.6d:* an iron mortar 5 *s.* [*sic*]	10	0	
1 iron pot & 2 pothooks 9*s.6d:* to bras skil- let 8*s.*		17	6
1 iron skillet: 4*s:* to bras kettles 1 *li:*	1	4	0
Chimney hoke or tramill 8*s:* 2 iron dogs 8*s*		16	0
a gridiron 3*s:* a fier pan 1*s:6d:* ballos 1*s* 6*d*		6	0
a Chaffing dish 1*s* to box irons 3*s:* a spit 3*s*		7	0
a bras candle stick: 1*s.* 3 bibles 12*s*		13	0
& other books 10*s;* to iron bullets 3*s.* a chest and a sifting trofe		10	0
in the innar roome: the bed & beding	3	2	0
a flax Comb 12*s:* a pair of loomes & harnis	4	12	0
in yarn 1 *li:2s:6d:* a quil wheele 2*s:6d:*	1	5	0
beere barrels & tunnil [funnel] 7*s:6d:* a friing pan		9	6
in the lento. [and] Ceelars trais & tubs & other lumber	1	18	6
in the Chambars; 4 sickles 2*s:* hoos 6*s:* a fro. [a cleaving tool] 3*s* [*sic*]	15	0	
Chaines & hoks: 14*s:6d:* a bend [a fetter] 8*s:* siths 5*s*	1	7	6
weges axles & other iron things		19	0
Cotton woole 6*s:* flax 16*s:* sheeps wool 20*s*	2	2	0
Cards 7*s:* 2 buts 5*s:* Spinning wheeles 14*s*	1	6	0
Warping bars & scarlet 6*s:* & other lumbars	1	6	0

71

Saddle & bridle	I	O	O
an iron Cettle	I	O	O
one plow & sheare & coulter Cope		IO	O
Cart & wheels	I	O	O
one musket & sword	I	O	O
3 oxen IO *li:* 6 Cowes I5 *li*	25	O	O
2 Calves I8*s:* 5 pigs I *li:* 5*s:*	2	3	O
one horse	5	O	O
	93	I	6

and as for Deetes that ar owing to this estate or that are to be payd from it Mrs Lumkin knows very littell Difference: and they are not much ether of them so far as she knowes

A Note on Sources

TWO TYPES OF SOURCES are basic to the study of agriculture in any given time or place. On the one hand, there are the writings of general observers of the countryside. Among these one finds travelers such as John Josselyn, whose very full *An Account of Two Voyages to New-England* (London, 1675) has been reprinted in the Massachusetts Historical Society's *Collections*, 3rd Ser., Vol. III (1833), and Edward Ward, author of *A Trip to New-England with a Character of the Country and People* (London, 1699). There are agricultural writers such as the sixteenth century's Thomas Tusser, whose various *Hundreth Good Pointes of Husbandrie* and *Five Hundreth Pointes of Good Husbandry* are readily available in Dorothy Hartley's *Thomas Tusser: His Good Points of Husbandry* (London, 1931), and the seventeenth century's prolific Gervase Markham. That such general observations have their faults as historical sources has been pointed out in the text. Travelers tended to exaggerate generally, and specifically, to exaggerate the unusual. Agricultural writers such as Markham were the avant-garde of their time, more often than not instructing contemporary farmers in the best practices (much as the Department of Agriculture does today) rather than reflecting what the farmers were really doing. Nevertheless travelers and agricultural writers are vital. G. E. Fussell's *The Old English Farming Books from Fitzherbert to Tull, 1523 to 1730* (London,

73

1947) is an excellent guide to the latter; R. W. G. Vail's *The Voice of the Old Frontier* (Philadelphia, 1949), to the former. Almanacs are normally of greater value than either, but only occasionally prior to Samuel Clough's *New England Almanack* (Boston, 1702) did New England's printers pay attention to the farmer; hence their value to this particular study has been limited.

General observations are particularly important for the very first years of the Plymouth colony, the period when official records are extremely scant. Vail lists many of these, but the most important are the so-called *Mourt's Relation— A Relation or Journall of the Beginning and Proceedings of the English Plantation Setled at Plimoth in New England* (London, 1622); E[dward] W[inslow]'s *Good Newes from New-England* (London, 1624); and the descriptive letters of John Pory (written in 1622 and 1623), Emmanuel Altham (1623, 1624, 1625), and Isaack de Rasieres (*ca.* 1628). *Mourt's* and Winslow's accounts have been printed with other pertinent material in *The Story of the Pilgrim Fathers, 1606–1623,* edited by Edward Arber (London, Boston, New York, 1897), and in *Chronicles of the Pilgrim Fathers,* compiled by Alexander Young (Boston, 1844); the Pory, Altham, and de Rasieres letters have been brought together by Sydney V. James, Jr., in his *Three Visitors to Early Plymouth* ([Plymouth], 1963). The various writings of Captain John Smith are of value, too, and are best consulted in the two-volume, Edinburgh, 1910 edition of the *Travels and Works of Captain John Smith,* edited by Edward Arber and A. G. Bradley. Governor William Bradford's *Of Plymouth Plantation, 1620–1647* is invaluable, the edition prepared by Samuel Eliot Morison (New York, 1953), although lacking some of the rich notes of earlier editions, being both the most complete and most readable. The governor's letters printed in "Governor [William]

Bradford's Letter Book," Massachusetts Historical Society, *Collections,* 1st Ser., Vol. III (1794), have some information.

The records of individual farmers constitute a second type of source for agricultural history, and one more directly pertinent to the locale and time, for ideally the story of agriculture is a composite of individual stories. But individuals as unimportant as farmers (and in Plymouth colony, very frequently only part-time farmers) leave little trace in the historical record. Common folk seldom wrote either letters or diaries or kept farm accounts, while the chances of such surviving to the present to become "historical evidence" are poor indeed. Some material exists, but not specifically for Plymouth. We can, however, extrapolate from such works as *The Diary of Thomas Minor of Stonington, Connecticut, 1653–1684,* edited by S. H. Miner and G. D. Stanton, Jr. (New London, 1899), and John Winthrop, Jr.'s report to the Royal Society on "Indian Corne" printed in Fulmer Mood's "John Winthrop, Jr., on Indian Corn," *New England Quarterly,* Vol. X (1937), assuming that the practices in nearby Connecticut towns were not radically different from those in the Old Colony. Similarly, Vol. I of the Massachusetts Archives, Boston, Massachusetts—"Agriculture, etc., 1644–1774"—and occasional other items dealing with Massachusetts Bay can be applied to New Plymouth.

Most important in this connection, however, and existing in quantity for Plymouth Colony, are the various official records pertaining to individual farmers, in particular the legal records of land transactions and probate proceedings. Directly, such material tells very little. But to a reader educated by travelers, diarists, and English agricultural writers to contemporary terminology and practices, it tells a great deal. The careful perusal and analysis of these records are the foundation of this study. The volumes of Plymouth *Court Orders, Deeds, &c., Miscellaneous Records* have been edited by Nathaniel B. Shurtleff and David Pulsifer and published as *Records of the Colony of New Plymouth in New England* [*1620–1692*], 12 vols. (Boston, 1855–61). Many of Plymouth's towns (now, of course, Massachusetts towns) have published their local records, most notably Plymouth itself: *Records of the Town of Plymouth*, 3 vols., edited by William T. Davis, *et al.* (Plymouth, 1889–1903). In addition, there are many local histories which extract liberally from town records: Richard LeBaron Bowen's *Early Rehoboth*, 4 vols. (Rehoboth, 1945–1950), for example; Samuel Deane's *History of Scituate, Massachusetts, from Its First Settlement to 1831* (Boston, 1831); and *Marshfield: The Autobiography of a Pilgrim Town* (Marshfield, 1940). A number of wills and inventories have been published in *The Plymouth Scrap Book*, edited by Charles Henry Pope (Boston, 1918) and still more in the volumes of *The Mayflower Descendant*. These last have been transcribed in full and, in typescript form, are on deposit at Pilgrim Hall, Plymouth, as "Plymouth Colony, Wills and Inventories."

There is a large secondary literature on early American agriculture, from special studies such as U. P. Hedrick's *History of Horticulture in America to 1860* (New York, 1950) and Robert Walcott's excellent "Husbandry in Colonial New England," *New England Quarterly*, Vol. IX (1936) to the more general works of Percy Wells Bidwell and John I. Falconer, *History of Agriculture in the Northern United States, 1620–1860* (New York, 1941) and the definitely inferior Lyman Carrier's *The Beginnings of Agriculture in America* (New York and London, 1923). The works of antiquarians are many and occasionally helpful, particularly George Francis Dow's *Every Day Life in the Massachusetts Colony* (Boston, 1935). The prolific Alice Morse Earle, whose *Home Life in Colonial Days* (New York, 1898) is but one of many works, wrote an indiscriminate "pots-and-pans" type social history which can be useful if approached with care. Bernard Bailyn's *The New England Merchants in the Seventeenth Century* (Cambridge, Mass., 1955) and the present author's "Governor Winthrop's Garden Crop: The Significance of Agriculture in the Early Commerce of Massachusetts Bay," *William and Mary Quarterly*, 3rd Ser., Vol. XX (1963) are useful in placing Plymouth's agricultural economy within the larger picture of the Atlantic community.

The secondary literature on early English agriculture is even more extensive. But too many of the English commentators have been too prone to accept the writings of the agricultural pamphleteers at face value and presume that the practices they advocated were the practices of the farmers. M. E. Seebohm's consciousness of the limitations of his sources throughout *The Evolution of the English Farm* (London, 1927) makes this the best of many works dealing with farm life. Rowland E. Prothero, Lord Ernle's *English Farming Past and Present* (New York, 1912) is older but still useful. Less involved with everyday living, but not to be overlooked, are G. E. Fussell and V. G. B. Atwater's "Agriculture of Rural England in the Seventeenth Century," *Economic Geography*, Vol. IX (1933); Joan Thirsk's *English Peasant Farming: The Agrarian History of Lincolnshire from Tudor to Recent Times* (London, 1957); W. G. Hoskins' "The Leicestershire Farmer in the 16th Century," Leicestershire Archaeological Society, *Transactions*, Vol. XXII (1941–42); and Mildred Campbell's *The English Yeoman under Elizabeth and the Early Stuarts* (New Haven,

1942). With her *The English Housewife in the Seventeenth Century* (London, 1953), Christina Hole is a peer of Alice Morse Earle.

The agricultural practices of the American Indian have, again, been exhaustively studied. M. K. Bennett's "The Food Economy of the New England Indians, 1605–75," *Journal of Political Economy*, Vol. LXIII (1955) is excellent, as is Charles C. Willoughby's *Antiquities of the New England Indians* (Cambridge, Mass., 1935); but one can do no better than to sample Indian life and culture as the seventeenth-century Englishman himself saw it. By far the best work for this purpose is Roger Williams' *A Key into the Language of America* (London, 1643), readily consulted in *The Complete Writings of Roger Williams*, 7 vols. edited by Reuben Aldridge Guild, *et al.* (New York, 1963).

There are no good general histories of Plymouth Colony, a phenomenon which Samuel Eliot Morison has pointed out in rather forceful terms in his "New Light Wanted on the Old Colony," *William and Mary Quarterly*, 3rd Ser., Vol. XV (1958). Morison's own *The Story of the "Old Colony" of New Plymouth* (New York, 1956)—written, as he himself noted, "for young people of all ages"—is the best, although the most complete narrative is still to be found in John Gorham Palfrey's *History of New England during the Stuart Dynasty*, 3 vols. (Boston, 1859).

Notes

CHAPTER ONE

"By Which Means They Were Scattered All over the Bay"

1. Nathaniel B. Shurtleff and David Pulsifer, eds., *Records of the Colony of New Plymouth in New England [1620–1692]*, *Plymouth Court Orders, 1661–1668* (Boston, 1855–61), pp. 70–71. All dates are given Old Style (Julian) except the year dates which have been modernized to make January 1 rather than March 25 New Year's Day. To transpose the days of the month to New Style (Gregorian), add ten days. Where applicable, both Old and New Style year dates are given in the notes.

2. See G. E. Fussell, "Social and Agrarian Background of the Pilgrim Fathers," *Agricultural History*, Vol. VII (1933), pp. 183–202.

3. William Bradford, *Of Plymouth Plantation, 1620–1647*, Samuel Eliot Morison, ed. (New York, 1953), p. 11; Bradford Smith, *Bradford of Plymouth* (Philadelphia and New York, 1951), pp. 28–39; John Brown, *The Pilgrim Fathers of New England and their Puritan Successors* (New York, Chicago, Toronto, 1896), pp. 54ff.; Charles Edward Banks, *The English Ancestry and Homes of the Pilgrim Fathers* (New York, 1929), pp. 65, 98–99.

4. Darrett B. Rutman, "The Pilgrims and Their Harbor," *William and Mary Quarterly*, 3rd Ser., Vol. XVII (1960), pp. 180–181.

5. *A Relation or Journall of the Beginning and Proceedings of the English Plantation Setled at Plimoth in New*

England (London, 1622)—best known as *Mourt's Relation*, and hereafter cited as such—as reprinted in Edward Arber, ed., *The Story of the Pilgrim Fathers, 1606–1623* (London, Boston, New York, 1897), p. 455.

6. *Ibid.*, p. 488; John Smith, *New Englands Trial* (London, 1622), as reprinted in Edward Arber and A. G. Bradley, eds., *Travels and Works of Captain John Smith* (Edinburgh, 1910), Vol. I, p. 264; Shurtleff and Pulsifer, eds., *Rec. of New Plymouth, Deeds, &c., 1620–1651,* pp. 4–6.

7. Ruth A. McIntyre, *Debts Hopeful and Desperate: Financing the Plymouth Colony* (Plymouth, 1963) is the best discussion of the relations between the settlers and their merchant backers.

8. *Mourt's Relation*, pp. 440–441. The formula was a garden plot 8½′ x 49½′ per person.

9. Bradford, *Plymouth Plantation*, p. 141; Robert Cushman to Bradford, December 22, 1624, "Governor [William] Bradford's Letter Book," Massachusetts Historical Society, *Collections*, 1st Ser., Vol. III (1794), p. 35; Shurtleff and Pulsifer, eds., *Rec. of New Plymouth, Deeds, &c., 1620–1651,* pp. 9–13, 32. Morison's reference to horses arriving in 1625 in Bradford, *Plymouth Plantation*, p. 174*n*, is fallacious; his evidence is Cushman's letter of December 22, 1624, but the "three or four jades [worn-out horses] to be sold unto you" which Cushman mentions were obviously never dispatched.

10. E[dward] W[inslow], *Good Newes from New-England* (London, 1624), as reprinted in Arber, ed., *Story of the Pilgrim Fathers*, p. 576; Bradford, *Plymouth Plantation*, p. 120; Bradford to Cushman, June 9, 1625, "Bradford's Letter Book," p. 36.

11. There are, basically, but two methods of sowing, seed-for-seed, or drill, and an indiscriminate scattering, or broadcast. The latter was part of the English agricultural tradition at the time Plymouth was settled; the former was not, although agricultural writers were attempting to intro-

duce the practice. The force of English tradition would have required the settlers to attempt to plant traditional grains in a traditional way. That without plows, reduced in number, and individually in a weakened condition, they did a bad job of it is clear from the poor harvest that year. See *infra*.

12. Roger Williams, *A Key into the Language of America* (London, 1643), as reprinted in Reuben Aldridge Guild, *et al.*, eds., *The Complete Writings of Roger Williams* (New York, 1963), Vol. I, p. 114.

13. A good, concise description is that of Isaack de Rasieres to Samuel Blommaert, *ca.* 1628, in Sydney V. James, Jr., ed., *Three Visitors to Early Plymouth* ([Plymouth], 1963), pp. 71–72, 78. See also M. K. Bennett, "The Food Economy of the New England Indians, 1605–75," *Journal of Political Economy*, Vol. LXIII (1955), pp. 369–397, and Erhard Rosthund, "The Evidence for the Use of Fish as Fertilizer in Aboriginal North America," *Journal of Geography*, Vol. LVI (1957), pp. 222–228. Rosthund doubts the widespread use of fish as fertilizer among the Indians. On Indian life and artifacts in general see Charles C. Willoughby, *Antiquities of the New England Indians* (Cambridge, Mass., 1935).

14. *Mourt's Relation*, pp. 414–415, 419–420; Bradford, *Plymouth Plantation*, pp. 65–66.

15. The story of Squanto is based on Bradford, *Plymouth Plantation*, p. 85.

16. Fulmer Mood, "John Winthrop, Jr., on Indian Corn," *New England Quarterly*, Vol. X (1937), pp. 121–133.

17. P. 595.

18. The ballad is reprinted in Samuel Eliot Morison's delightful *The Story of the "Old Colony" of New Plymouth* (New York, 1956), pp. 97–99.

19. *Mourt's Relation*, pp. 489, 493; W[inslow], *Good Newes from New England*, p. 594.

20. E.g., *The Journal of Madam Knight* (New York, 1935), p. 25.

21. It is frequently stated that private property—defined in terms of fee tenure—was not introduced until 1627. This is based upon a misreading of the pertinent records of the grants of 1624 and 1627 found in Bradford, *Plymouth Plantation*, p. 145, and Shurtleff and Pulsifer, eds., *Rec. of New Plymouth, Laws, 1623–1682*, p. 4. Bradford, referring to the 1624 grants, wrote "to every person was given only one acre of land, to them and theirs." The *Laws* relative to the 1627 grants reads "That the first division of the acres should stand and continue f[irm according] to the former division made unto the possessors thereof and to their heires for ever." In order to say that bequeathable grants, and thus private property, were not made until 1627 one has to ignore Bradford's "to them and theirs" and read the *Laws* as though a comma stood between "thereof" and "and," thus making "to their heires for ever" something additional to what was granted in "the former division made unto the possessors." Yet Bradford's "to them and theirs" does exist and does imply "to them and their heirs"; there is no comma in the provision of the *Laws*, and therefore it has to be understood that the former division referred to is that of 1624 "to them and theirs," *i.e.*, to the possessors and their heirs forever.

22. Bradford, *Plymouth Plantation*, pp. 120, 132–133, 145, 187–188; W[inslow], *Good Newes from New-England*, p. 576; Shurtleff and Pulsifer, eds., *Rec. of New Plymouth, Deeds, &c., 1620–1651*, pp. 4–14. Note the discrepancy between Bradford, p. 187, in which an absolutely equal distribution is described, and *Deeds, &c., 1620–1651*, pp. 9–14, in which the division is unequal among the "families." The latter should be accounted "best evidence."

23. Bradford, *Plymouth Plantation*, pp. 120, 144–145; de Rasieres to Blommaert, *ca.* 1628, James, ed., *Three Visitors*, pp. 77–78; John Smith, *Advertisements for the Unexperienced Planters of New England* (London, 1631), in Arber and Bradley, eds., *Works of Captain John Smith*,

Vol. II, p. 954. Smith exaggerates the population of 1630, writing "betwixt foure or five hundred."

24. *Mourt's Relation*, p. 466.

25. Darrett B. Rutman, *Winthrop's Boston: Portrait of a Puritan Town, 1630–1649* (Chapel Hill, 1965), pp. 178ff.; *idem*, "Governor Winthrop's Garden Crop: The Significance of Agriculture in the Early Commerce of Massachusetts Bay," *William and Mary Quarterly*, 3rd Ser., Vol. XX (1963), pp. 396–415.

26. Real estate, cattle, and produce values can be traced in Shurtleff and Pulsifer, eds., *Rec. of New Plymouth*, particularly the Vols. *Deeds, &c., 1620–1651, Court Orders, 1633–1640*, and *Court Orders, 1641–1651*, and in the typescript "Plymouth Colony, Wills and Inventories," Vol. I, 1620–1639, and Vol. II, 1641–1649, in Pilgrim Hall, Plymouth, Mass.

27. Bradford, *Plymouth Plantation*, p. 253.

28. *Ibid.*, pp. 253–254. See also John Reyner and William Brewster "in the name and with the consent of the rest" of the Plymouth Church to the "reverende brethren the church of Christ in Boston to the Elders there," August 5, 1639, John Cotton Papers, Prince Collection, Boston Public Library, Boston, Mass., which complains of "the holding of Farmes" by Plymouth men as detrimental to church unity.

29. Bradford, *Plymouth Plantation*, pp. 253–254; Shurtleff and Pulsifer, eds., *Rec. of New Plymouth, Court Orders, 1633–1640*, p. 17.

30. Based upon the computations of Richard LeBaron Bowen in *Early Rehoboth* (Rehoboth, 1945–50), Vol. I, Chap. 1.

31. Rutman, "Governor Winthrop's Garden Crop," pp. 398ff., and the survey of values cited in note 26 above.

32. Shurtleff and Pulsifer, eds., *Rec. of New Plymouth, Deeds, &c., 1620–1651*, p. 60.

33. The decline of fish as a fertilizer is indicated by the

gradual disinvolvement of the towns from the fish weirs, the transferal of the weirs to private persons, and, ultimately, the state of disrepair of the weirs—all of which can be traced in various town records. On the other hand, the increased use of manure is reflected in the increased mentions of it in *ibid.*, e.g., pp. 60, 118, 126.

34. One can follow this progression in William T. Davis, *et al.*, eds., *Records of the Town of Plymouth* (Plymouth, 1889–1903), Vol. I, in the records and to a lesser extent the published histories of other Old Colony towns, and, from the standpoint of efforts to curb the semiwild cattle, in the various volumes of Shurtleff and Pulsifer, eds., *Rec. of New Plymouth, Court Orders.*

35. *Ibid., Court Orders, 1641–1651*, p. 60. *Cf.* the order of 1635, prior to Plymouth's complete subjugation to the Bay's economy, in *ibid., Court Orders, 1633–1640*, pp. 34–35: "It was decreed that the new bushell (being a seald bushell brought out of England, of Winchester measure) should be allowed, and no other." Note, too, the provisions in the "Treasury Accounts" of later in the century for the payment of taxes in "country pay" to the treasurer at either Plymouth or Boston (*ibid., Miscellaneous Records, 1633–1689*, pp. 123, 130–131, 142, 146, 153).

36. Samuel Maverick, "A Briefe Discription of New England and the Severall Townes therein," *ca.* 1660, in Mass. Hist. Soc., *Proceedings*, 2nd Ser., Vol. I (1885), pp. 243–244.

37. "A true Inventory of the estate of Mr John Barnes . . . ," August 30, 1671, Charles Henry Pope, ed., *The Plymouth Scrap Book* (Boston, 1918), pp. 102–108.

38. Rutman, "Governor Winthrop's Garden Crop," pp. 404–406. The credit network of the Atlantic is excellently described in Bernard Bailyn, *The New England Merchants in the Seventeenth Century* (Cambridge, Mass., 1955).

39. Shurtleff and Pulsifer, eds., *Rec. of New Plymouth, Court Orders, 1633–1640*, p. 137, *1641–1651*, p. 5. The

normal price differential for grain between Boston and Plymouth was 6*d*. per bushel.

40. Bowen, *Rehoboth*, Vol. I, p. 20.

41. One suspects that other areas of New England had less of it than is generally suggested. Boston certainly did not fit the classic pattern, even in its early years. See Rutman, *Winthrop's Boston*, pp. 93ff. *et passim*.

42. A term generally used, *e.g.*, Shurtleff and Pulsifer, eds., *Rec. of New Plymouth, Court Orders, 1661–1668*, p. 40, referring to "the naighbourhood att Acushena" and "the naighbourhood of Sowamsett."

43. *Ibid.*, p. 65, *1678–1691*, pp. 67, 72, 189.

44. Davis, *et al.*, eds., *Rec. of the Town of Plymouth*, p. 29. Plymouth's "naighbourhoods" are reflected throughout the town records.

45. Even a town as neatly laid out in four- and five-acre houselots, as Scituate was initially, in actuality was a straggling collection of neighborhoods. Its neat order was at the very beginning marred by Humphrey Turner's "house and farm," minister John Lothrop's twenty-acre farm, Isaac Robinson's twelve acres; in only a short time it would be further marred by the 200-acre farms of Timothy Hatherly and John Williams and the isolated house of William Wills on Tongue Island. The examples could be multiplied. See Samuel Deane, *History of Scituate* (Boston, 1831), pp. 9–10, 281, 384–385.

46. Shurtleff and Pulsifer, eds., *Rec. of New Plymouth, Court Orders, 1641–1651*, pp. 78, 119; *Deeds, &c., 1620–1651*, p. 152.

47. *Ibid., Court Orders, 1633–1640*, pp. 24, 40, 56–57, 71, 120, 136, 154, *1641–1651*, p. 13, *1668–1678*, p. 88, *Deeds, &c., 1620–1651*, pp. 214–215; Davis, *et al.*, eds., *Rec. of the Town of Plymouth*, p. 13 *et passim*; "A true Inventory of the estate of Mr John Barnes . . . ," August 30, 1671, Pope, ed., *Plymouth Scrap Book*, pp. 102–108.

48. Shurtleff and Pulsifer, eds., *Rec. of New Plymouth,*

Court Orders, 1633–1640, p. 86, *1651–1661,* pp. 159, 181, 219, 222, *1661–1668,* p. 136, *1668–1678,* pp. 61, 80–81, *Deeds, &c., 1620–1651,* pp. 106–107, 110, 111, 114, 152, 157, 213; Davis, *et al.,* eds., *Rec. of the Town of Plymouth,* p. 20 *et passim;* "A true Inventory of the Estate of Gyles Rickard senior . . . ," February 6, 1684/85, Pope, ed., *Plymouth Scrap Book,* pp. 49–50.

49. Shurtleff and Pulsifier, eds., *Rec. of New Plymouth, Court Orders, 1668–1678,* p. 273; "An Inventory of the Estate of mr francis Combe . . . ," January 5, 1682/83, Pope, ed., *Plymouth Scrap Book,* pp. 27–28.

50. Samuel Eliot Morison, "New Light Wanted on the Old Colony," *William and Mary Quarterly,* 3rd Ser., Vol. XV (1958), p. 363.

CHAPTER TWO

Wills and Inventories: The Reconstructed Farm

1. John Josselyn, *An Account of Two Voyages to New-England* (London, 1675), reprinted in Mass. Hist. Soc., *Collections,* 3rd Ser., Vol. III (1833), pp. 249–250.

2. Three representative inventories are included in the appendix. An excellent guide to English agricultural writers is G. E. Fussell, *The Old English Farming Books from Fitzherbert to Tull, 1523 to 1730* (London, 1947); to travel accounts and descriptive pamphlets, R. W. G. Vail, *The Voice of the Old Frontier* (Philadelphia, 1949); to diaries, William Mathews, *American Diaries: An Annotated Bibliography of American Diaries prior to . . . 1861* (Berkeley, 1945) and H. M. Forbes, *New England Diaries, 1602–1800* (Topsfield, Mass., 1923).

3. George Francis Dow, *Every Day Life in the Massachusetts Bay Colony* (Boston, 1935), Chap. 2. See also the standard studies of architecture in the period: Hugh S. Morrison, *Early American Architecture, from the First Colonial*

Settlements to the National Period (New York, 1952); Fiske Kimball, *Domestic Architecture of the American Colonies and of the Early Republic* (New York, 1922); Harold R. Shurtleff, *The Log Cabin Myth* (Cambridge, Mass., 1939).

4. "A true Inventory of all the goods chattells and cattells wch were mr John Jenneys . . . ," May 25, 1644, "Plymouth Colony, Wills and Inventories." Although drawn from Suffolk County, Massachusetts, Abbott Lowell Cummings, ed., *Rural Household Inventories: Establishing the Names, Uses, and Furnishings of Rooms in the Colonial New England Home, 1675–1775* (Boston, 1964) gives the flavor of the interior of the Plymouth home as well.

5. E. N. Hartley, *Ironworks on the Saugus* (Norman, Okla., 1957), p. 257.

6. M. E. Seebohm, *The Evolution of the English Farm* (London, 1927), pp. 226, 258–259; Lyman Carrier, *The Beginnings of Agriculture in America* (New York and London, 1923), pp. 263–265.

7. See, *e.g.*, "An Inventory of all the goods and Chatells of William Launders . . . ," January 1, 1648/49, "Plymouth Colony, Wills and Inventories," while "An Inventory of the Estate of mr francis Combe . . . ," January 5, 1682/83, Pope, ed., *Plymouth Scrap Book,* p. 27, lists "The wood of a plough."

8. Carrier, *Beginnings of Agriculture in America,* pp. 265, 266.

9. "The Inventory of Henery Smith . . . ," December 21, 1647, "Plymouth Colony, Wills and Inventories."

10. [Gervase] *Markhams Farewell to Husbandry* (London, 1656), pp. 60–61.

11. Robert R. Walcott, "Husbandry in Colonial New England," *New England Quarterly,* Vol. IX (1936), pp. 232–233.

12. Shurtleff and Pulsifer, eds., *Rec. of New Plymouth, Court Orders, 1661–1668,* pp. 117–118.

13. Dorothy Hartley, ed., *Thomas Tusser: His Good Points of Husbandry* (London, 1931), p. 58.

14. Other early stories about potatoes can be found in John Mitchell, *The Present State of Great Britain and North America* (London, 1767), p. 72.

15. A good sampling of gardening practices is to be found in Thomas Hill, *The Profitable Arte of Gardening* (London, 1568)—except for herbals, the first English book on gardening; in William Lawson's 1618 *A New Orchard and Garden* (London, 1927), which was appropriated by Gervase Markham as the sixth part of his *A Way to Get Wealth* (London, 1625); and in Leonard Meager, *The English Gardener* (London, 1670). The distinction between flower, herb, and vegetable gardens was beginning to be made in the seventeenth century, but in New as in Old England, the common house garden was the last to change from older ways.

16. Jane Strickland Hussey, "Notes on Pilgrim Herb Gardens," typescript, Plimoth Plantation, Inc., Plymouth, Mass.

17. Josselyn, *Two Voyages to New-England*, p. 337. See also George Fenwick to John Winthrop, May 6, 1641, Mass. Hist. Soc., *Winthrop Papers* (Boston, 1929–47), Vol. IV, p. 339, referring to the dissemination of fruit trees via seeds.

18. Fruit trees and orchards do not show up significantly in land transactions or inventories until the mid-1640's. The buds could also have come from the Bay Colony, orchards being found there in the early 1630's and at Salem even earlier—U. P. Hedrick, *A History of Horticulture in America to 1860*, New York, 1950, p. 25.

19. Shurtleff and Pulsifer, eds., *Rec. of New Plymouth, Deeds, &c., 1620–1651*, pp. 68–69, 112, 137, 213.

20. Roger Williams to John Winthrop, Jr., May 28, 1647, Guild, *et al.*, eds., *Complete Writings of Roger Williams*, Vol. VI, p. 147.

21. Josselyn, *Two Voyages to New-England*, pp. 337–

338; S. H. Miner and G. D. Stanton, Jr., eds., *The Diary of Thomas Minor of Stonington, Connecticut, 1653–1684* (New London, 1899), pp. 34, 64, 70, 80, 157; Samuel Danforth, *An Almanack* (Cambridge, Mass., 1647), under August and September; Samuel Clough, *New England Almanack* (Boston, 1702), under January, February, March. English orchard practices can be sampled in [Gervase Markham], *The Husbandmans Fruitfull Orchard* (London, 1637).

22. The combination of compact and dispersed holdings reflects in part the fact that Plymouth's settlers were from both the open and enclosed agricultural areas of England, areas well defined in Sumner Chilton Powell, *Puritan Village: The Formation of a New England Town* (Middletown, Conn., 1963).

23. Ralph H. Brown, *Historical Geography of the United States* (New York, 1948), p. 108; Rutman, "Pilgrims and Their Harbor," p. 180; Morison, *Story of the Old Colony*, p. 146. See also *Marshfield: The Autobiography of a Pilgrim Town* (Marshfield, 1940), Chap. 1.

24. "Report of Edmund Browne [to Sir Simonds D'Ewes, September, 1639]," Colonial Society of Massachusetts, *Publications*, Vol. VII (1905), pp. 76–80.

25. *I.e.*, "remove all saplings." Jared Eliot, *Essays on Field-Husbandry in New England* (Boston, 1760), p. 1.

26. "An Inventorie of the goods and chattells of Nathaniell Tilden . . . ," July 31, 1641; "A true Inventory of all the goods and Chattells moveable of mr Willm Kemp . . . ," September 23, 1641: both in "Plymouth Colony, Wills and Inventories." The method is not perfect. Appraisers might differ in judgment; the estimated size of a field given by an appraiser might be off; the time of year might affect the appraisal—*e.g.*, a July field, with the summer's hazards still ahead might be valued less than the same field in September. A margin for error must, therefore, be allowed.

27. To be found in Pope, ed., *Plymouth Scrap Book* and "Plymouth Colony, Wills and Inventories."

28. Percy Wells Bidwell and John I. Falconer, *History of Agriculture in the Northern United States, 1620–1860* (New York, 1941), p. 14; Thomas Hutchinson, *The History of the Colony and Province of Massachusetts-Bay,* Lawrence Shaw Mayo, ed. (Cambridge, Mass., 1936), Vol. I, p. 404; Draft letter from the General Court of Massachusetts Bay to Edward Winslow in England, *ca.* 1650, Massachusetts Archives, Boston, Mass., Vol. CVI. These yields can be compared to modern yields—and are, *infra*—for the standard Bay bushel in use was roughly equivalent to the English Winchester bushel, which, in turn, is roughly equivalent to the current bushel measure in the United States. The British imperial bushel is somewhat larger.

29. "An Inventory of the estate of Ephraim hicks . . . ," March 6, 1649/50, "Plymouth Colony, Wills and Inventories."

30. Rutman, "Governor Winthrop's Garden Crop," pp. 411–412*n.*

31. ". . . a true Inventory of all the goods and cattells of the said John Briggs . . . ," *ca.* June, 1641; "The Will of Grace Granger": both in "Plymouth Colony, Wills and Inventories"; "The Inventory of the Estate of James Bell . . . ," March 5, 1676/77, Pope, ed., *Plymouth Scrap Book,* pp. 124–125. The Lumkin inventory is included in the appendix.

32. Seebohm, *Evolution of the English Farm,* pp. 246ff.; Bidwell and Falconer, *Agriculture in the Northern United States,* pp. 24–25. *Cf.* the actual description of early Plymouth cattle in the records, e.g., Shurtleff and Pulsifer, eds., *Rec. of New Plymouth, Deeds, &c., 1620–1651,* pp. 9ff.

33. "The Last Will and Testament of Thomas Blise . . . ," October 7, 1647, "Plymouth Colony, Wills and Inventories."

34. Seebohm, *Evolution of the English Farm,* p. 219.

35. [Gervase Markham], *Cheape and Good Husbandry for the Well-Ordering of all Beasts and Fowles* (London, 1653), pp. 87–97.

36. Such laws run throughout the colony and various town records.

37. [Markham], *Cheape and Good Husbandry*, pp. 142–145.

38. Seebohm, *Evolution of the English Farm*, pp. 247–248. G. E. Fussell and V. G. B. Atwater, "Agriculture of Rural England in the Seventeenth Century," *Economic Geography*, Vol. IX (1933), p. 381, indicates the success of breeding for size. Early in the century about 600 pounds seems to have been the average weight of neat cattle; by the end of the century some were up to 900 and 1,000 pounds.

39. Mood, "John Winthrop, Jr., on Indian Corn," pp. 125–129. One can reconstruct the agricultural year using such sources as Miner and Stanton, eds., *Diary of Thomas Minor*, and Clough, *New England Almanack* [1702].

40. Walcott, "Husbandry in Colonial New England," pp. 231–232.

41. Mood, "John Winthrop, Jr., on Indian Corn," p. 128.

42. Seebohm, *Evolution of the English Farm*, p. 228; Walcott, "Husbandry in Colonial New England," pp. 238–239.

43. Hutchinson, *History*, Vol. I, p. 406*n*.

44. Seebohm, *Evolution of the English Farm*, p. 268.

45. [Edward Ward], *A Trip to New-England with a Character of the Country and People* (London, 1699), p. 11.

46. Seebohm, *Evolution of the English Farm*, p. 263. See also G. E. Fussell, "Four Centuries of Leicestershire Farming," in W. G. Hoskins, *Studies in Leicestershire Agrarian History* (Leicester, Eng., 1949), p. 164, giving 1770 yields.

47. *Cf.* the more generally accepted figures of twenty

and twenty-five bushels in Rutman, "Governor Winthrop's Garden Crop," p. 411 and *n.*

48. Seebohm, *Evolution of the English Farm,* pp. 173, 230, and *n.* M. K. Bennett, "British Wheat Yield per Acre for Seven Centuries," *Economic History,* Vol. III (1935), pp. 12–29.

49. Letter of Thomas Graves (1629) in [Francis] Higginson, *New Englands Plantation* (London, 1630), reprinted in Mass. Hist. Soc., *Proceedings,* Vol. LXII (1930), p. 318; Martin Pring, quoted in Rutman, "Pilgrims and Their Harbor," p. 168.

50. Hutchinson, *History,* Vol. I, p. 404.

51. William Wood's 1634 *New Englands Prospect* (Boston, 1865), p. 14; William Hubbard, *General History of New England,* Mass. Hist. Soc., *Collections,* 2d Ser., Vol. V (1815), p. 23.

52. Hartley, ed., *Tusser,* p. 101.

53. *Ibid.,* p. 7, and *cf.* pp. 142–144, 145–147.

54. See Fussell's survey of this literature in *Old English Farming Books,* Chaps. 3, 4, 5; Rowland E. Prothero, Lord Ernle, *English Farming, Past and Present* (New York, 1912), pp. 105ff.

55. Fussell illustrates this device in *Old English Farming Books,* opposite p. 80.

56. Mood, "John Winthrop, Jr., on Indian Corn," pp. 121–123.

57. In [Samuel Hartlib], *An Essay for the Advancement of Husbandry-Learning or Propositions for the Erecting a Colledge of Husbandry* (London, 1651).

58. "Husbandry in Colonial New England," p. 224.

59. "An Inventory of the goods & Chattels of Samuel Fuller . . . ," January 2 [1633], "Plymouth Colony, Wills and Inventories." Neither Godfridus' *The Knowledge of Things Unknowne with the Husbandmans Practise* (London, 1619) nor Goad's *The Dolefull Even Song* (London, 1623) was sufficiently agricultural in nature to warrant

inclusion in Fussell, *Old English Farming Books*. The first is a compendium of "prognostications" and weather signs; the second, without any agricultural connotations whatever. There are other possibilities—Bishop Grosstete, Barnaby Googe, for example—but all equally useless.

60. Roger Williams to John Winthrop, Jr., May 28, 1647, Guild, *et al.*, eds., *Writings of Roger Williams*, Vol. VI, pp. 146–147. See also Josselyn, *Two Voyages to New England*, p. 336: "Our English *Clover-grass*, sowen thrives very well."

61. P. 10. Ward tended to quip more than describe and must be utilized with care; *e.g.*, he continues, "for every Hour he spends in his *Grounds* he will be two at an *Ordinary*. They have wonderful *Appetites*, and will Eat like *Plough-men*; tho very *Lazy*, and *Plough* like *Gentlemen:* It being no rarity there, to see a Man *Eat* till he *Sweats*, and *Work* till he *Freezes*."

62. Some have generalized that there was an *actual* turn to extensive agriculture. Thus Robert E. Gallman, *Developing the American Colonies, 1607–1783* (Chicago, 1964), p. 33, writes that while "advanced farming methods" were impossible under New World circumstances, the colonial farmers "made up for their primitive techniques by farming large stretches of the rich land." This is simply not the case in Plymouth, where average holdings were not radically above the size of English holdings and the farmer regularly cultivated only a part of what he held.

63. *New Englands Prospects*, p. 14.

CHAPTER THREE

Epilogue

1. For a short, incisive discussion of Plymouth's contributions, see George L. Haskins, "The Legacy of Plymouth," *Social Education*, Vol. XXVI (1962), pp. 7–13.

2. Charles M. Andrews, *The Colonial Period of American History: The Settlements* (New Haven, Conn., 1934–1937), Vol. I, pp. 298–299.

3. Morison, "New Light Wanted on the Old Colony," p. 359.

4. The first extensive study of Plymouth's history throughout the period of its independent existence, stressing the political scene, is George D. Langdon, Jr., *Pilgrim Colony: A History of New Plymouth, 1620–1691* (New Haven, 1966).

5. A factor recognized by John Demos in his "Notes on Life in Plymouth Colony," *William and Mary Quarterly*, 3rd Ser., Vol. XXII (1965), pp. 244–286, and by Plimoth Plantation in inaugurating this series of monographs.

Index

Index

Index

Nickerson, Nicholas, 20
North River, 27
Nurseries, 39

Oats, *see* Grains
Onions, 7, 37, 38
Orchards, 36, 38–41, 58, 61, 88
Oxen, *see* Animals

Parsnips, 7, 38
Pears, 39
Peas (field), *see* Grains
Peas (garden), 7
Pigs, *see* Animals
Plain Dealing, 23
Plat, Sir Hugh, 53, 56
Plows, *see* Farm equipment
Plums, 39, 40
Plymouth (colony): early settlement of, 3–7; economy, 3–4, 6–7, 11–17, 19–21, 26, 27, 60, 63, 64; population, 13, 14–15, 21, 63; development of towns in, 14–15, 17, 18–19, 21–23, 30, 42, 46–47, 60, 64; town structure in, 23–24, 85; merger with Massachusetts Bay, 27, 63
Plymouth (town), 44, 46; as settlement site, 5, 10, 42; land allotments in, 12, 13, 15, 17–18; population, 13, 14–15, 21, 23, 24; merchants in, 20; development of, 23–24, 30
Ponagausett, *see* Dartmouth, Mass.
Potatoes, 37–38
Poultry, *see* Animals
Prence, Thomas, 15

Private property, *see* Land
Pumpkins, 9, 29, 37, 46, 50, 52

Quinces, 39

Radishes, 7, 37
Reapers, 51
Rehoboth, Mass., 15, 20, 21, 26, 34, 42
Rhode Island, 64
Rickard, Gyles, 25–26, 40
Robinson, Isaac, 85
Rochester, Mass., 23, 24
Rocky Nook, 23
Roxbury, Mass., 13
Royal Society, 58
Russell, George, 40
Rye, *see* Grains

Saconessett, *see* Falmouth, Mass.
St. Mildred's Poultry, 56
Salem, Mass., 69, 88
Sandwich, Mass., 15, 21–23, 66
Scarecrows, 51
Scituate, Mass., 15, 21, 25, 26, 46, 85; merchants in, 20
Scythes, *see* Farm equipment
Seeds, 7, 10; transporting, 5, 39; method of planting, 7, 56, 80; treating, 56
Seekonk Plain, *see* Rehoboth, Mass.
Sepecan, *see* Rochester, Mass.
Servants, 12, 14, 25, 26, 50, 61, 69
Sheep, *see* Animals
Sherley, James, 6
Shipbuilding, 27
Shops, *see* Merchants

99

ERIC G. ENGSTROM 1966